Donato G. MacRae
London 1952.

THE WISDOM OF THE EAST SERIES

EDITED BY J. L. CRANMER-BYNG, M.C.

EASTERN SCIENCE

£1 —

Eastern Science

An Outline of its Scope and Contribution

By

H. J. J. WINTER, Ph.D., M.Sc.,
A.Inst.P., M.R.A.S.

John Murray, Albemarle Street,
London, W.

First Edition . . . 1952

Made and Printed in Great Britain by Butler & Tanner Ltd., Frome and London
and published by John Murray (Publishers) Ltd.

It is fitting then for us not to be ashamed to acknowledge truth and to assimilate it from whatever source it comes to us, even if it is brought to us by former generations and foreign peoples. For him who seeks the truth there is nothing of higher value than truth itself; it never cheapens nor abases him who searches for it, but ennobles and honours him.

AL-KINDĪ, Preface to *Metaphysics*
(trans. M. Guidi and R. Walzer).

EDITORIAL NOTE

The object of the editor of this series is a very definite one. He desires above all things that, in their humble way, these books shall be the ambassadors of good-will and understanding between East and West, the old world of Thought, and the new of Action. He is confident that a deeper knowledge of the great ideals and lofty philosophy of Oriental thought may help to a revival of that true spirit of Charity which neither despises nor fears the nations of another creed and colour.

J. L. CRANMER-BYNG.

50, Albemarle Street,
London, W.1.

CONTENTS

PAGE

Introduction 1

1. The Ancient Civilizations 5
   - (i) Babylonia and Assyria 6
   - (ii) Egypt 10
   - (iii) The Indus Valley, and the Hindu Successors . . 16
   - (iv) Ancient China 19

2. Mediaeval China 27

3. Mediaeval India 37

4. The Scope of Arabic Science 59
   - (i) The Arabic Period and the Diffusion of Science . 59
   - (ii) Some great Arabic thinkers and experimenters . 64
   - (iii) The Scientific Legacy of Islām to Latin Christendom 85

5. Modern Times : What Asian Science teaches us . 91

Select Bibliography 101

Index 107

INTRODUCTION

THE power of Science lies in a method. This inductive method is the means by which men interpret the working of God's laws in nature. Being a human interpretation it is penultimate and can merely explain in more and more exact terms how natural processes operate. Why natural laws take certain forms and not others is a question of ultimate cause : God only can know in full, and the order of nature is His.

Science however implies Faith, faith to rely upon the immutability of this Divine Order, and though Science may be regarded as supplementary to Religion, it cannot ultimately be in conflict with it. Thus behind the material world of transient phenomena perceived through the senses and explained by Science in terms of energy and time and space there is the Mystic Immanence, and it has been a characteristic of many of the great sages of the East that they have forsaken the former (Māyā) for the latter, and have claimed Truth by self-renunciation in God. The approach to Truth by way of scientific investigation of matter, which would seem to give no meaning to ultimate cause, was of doubtful appeal, and such an outlook has frequently coloured whatever attempts have been made in the scientific field in the East. It is therefore useful to regard the past history of Eastern science within its philosophical context, and to expect little emphasis upon technological development which the Western mind has to-day come to regard as the invariable deductive consequence of any new scientific discovery. The old term 'natural philosophy' might well be revived and applied to it.

Professor George Sarton has divided men into those who

understand and practise the experimental method and those who do not. Briefly, the process involves the impartial collection of facts *first, followed* by induction to give a natural law, *followed again* by deduction from which the consequences within the framework of the law are derived. The Western mind, which since the seventeenth century has pursued this method with ever-growing success, has sought to combat nature and to compel her to utilitarian ends. Let it not be forgotten, however, that there is another mind which has moved through countless centuries in a spirit of accceptance and co-operation with her. This mind sought Brahmā. But it also found algebra and trigonometry.

Only in such light can one come to understand Eastern science. Looking back behind the vast technological superstructure of Western civilization to a quieter day, one may discover certain Asian origins from which that growth sprang, and commune with those few men who understood and sometimes practised the experimental method in a world motivated by theological and philosophical tradition. Though their bones lie buried by the desert sand or rest in some quiet grave where the blossoms fall twice in the year, their thoughts accompany us still ; through the length of our schooldays they speak to us as we prepare for the complex world of tomorrow.

This little book sketches the mere tentative outline of a vast picture, many details of which are yet to be revealed. I fully realize that no really adequate work can yet be written on the scientific ideas of the East, and I shall be fully prepared to reconsider both my facts and judgments when more material becomes available. At present the greatest need is for translations of many more of the most important scientific writings of the East, translations made in accordance with the standards of the best modern scholarship. But this is a very slow process, and an interim statement does seem justifiable. Further, it may be objected that this small work is too concentrated, and is consequently out of focus. But it is meant as a brief introduction to the study of Eastern science, and by giving the reader the overall picture it is hoped to encourage him to undertake a more detailed examination himself of the particular subject which most interests him. My aim throughout has been to deal *only* with the *main* lines of development, and I have *tried* to keep a sense of balance. I take refuge with Sa'dī—sometimes " good gear may be contained in small parcels "—and if what I have written makes the reader want to know more, then his pleasure will also be mine. I have appended to the book a short bibliography of selected works which will start him on a hard but fascinating journey : whilst being in no way exhaustive, these works are representative and authoritative. No reference to sources of original manuscripts has been made at this stage, nor has an attempt been made to be rigidly consistent in the spelling of Oriental names. I have borrowed freely from many of the works listed and wish to record my deep indebtedness ; in particular, my obligation to Professor Sarton's monumental *Introduction to the History of Science* goes without question. I would also express my gratitude to Professor S. H. Watkins, Vice-Principal of University College, Exeter, who has kindly allowed me to pursue my researches into the Asian aspects of the history of science, as a source of teaching methods, and to which this little book is incidental. Finally, I thank all those Orientalists and historians of science from whom I have drawn inspiration and encouragement—Professor Sarton himself, Professor and Mrs. Charles Singer, Dr. Joseph Needham, F.R.S., Dr. H. E. Stapleton, Dr. E. J. Holmyard, Dr. A. Mieli, H. D. G. Law, Esq., C.I.E., Dr. R. Walzer, and my colleague Mr. W. 'Arafat, who first guided my steps in the language of the Prophet.

1. *THE ANCIENT CIVILIZATIONS*

The origin of the rationalization of man's views of the world was pre-Greek : thus the *phusis* associated with the Ionians and elaborated in a form of inductive inquiry by Aristotle and by Archimedes followed upon various hypotheses and technical achievements of the Empires of Antiquity. The inductive method by which Science adds to itself new knowledge requires both analysis (experiment) and synthesis (theory), and unless these aspects are closely correlated, hypotheses become isolated and sterile, and experiments but random novelties. It was the peculiar turn of the Greek genius which first made this correlation possible, working to some extent upon the data and the instruments bequeathed by its predecessors.

SETTLED communities first owed their establishment to the domestication of water, and it was in the River Valley Cultures of the Tigris-Euphrates, Nile, Indus, and Yellow River basins that the " tools " of Science came to be fashioned. These primary " tools " comprised a certain competence in the handling of natural materials and a degree of abstraction which resulted in writing and symbolism. Upon the former was developed a limited technology in metals and other substances and a competence in medical and surgical practice, whilst the latter made possible exact statement and the concept of number. It is significant that, with the Sumerians for instance, writing reaches some three thousand years further back than it does on the mainland of Greece.

Ancient Eastern cosmology is generally built upon the square and cube, whereas the Greeks thought in terms of the circle and sphere. This representation of, for example, planetary orbits in 'square' form led to a particular set of numbers obtained through the subdivision of the square, or rectangle, and distinct from π which is characteristic of the circle. These numbers, such as 4, 12, 28, 60, were used to build up a geometrical framework into which the astronomical phenomena were fitted, a process which is, however, the converse of scientific method. C. P. S. Menon considers their origin to have been a mathematical rather than an astronomical necessity. Eastern races have generally divided the equinoctial-ecliptic stars into 28 (or sometimes 27) groups ; we find this division in the literature of India (cf. the Atharva-Veda, the Taittirīya Brāhmaṇa) and China (Hsia Hsiao Cheng, Chou Li), and later in Arabia (pre-Qur'anic poetry).

(i) BABYLONIA AND ASSYRIA

The beginnings of Mesopotamian civilization and the origin of the practice of science (as distinct from the *concept* of Science of the Greeks) are intimately connected, and the earliest scientific records extant are those of Uruk, *c.* 3500 B.C. Here we see not only the transmission of writing but carefully recorded observations from which rudimentary classification and analysis of data were made, e.g. in the groupings of animals and plants. In this Sumerian, non-Semitic, culture of the Lower Tigris-Euphrates is to be found also the earliest cosmological speculation upon the universe, the creation of man, and the deluge.

There follows the Semitic Akkadian culture of Babylonia and Assyria. The Babylonian period as a whole was remarkable for its astronomical and mathematical achievements, the latter probably the most outstanding pre-Hellenist contributions to abstract thought, some of them algebraic in character. Whilst Ancient Egyptian Mathematics has engaged the attention of many scholars, Babylonian Mathematics is a comparatively new field of research with its own difficulties of interpretation : it is only a century ago that pioneer Assyriologists, Rawlinson,

Hincks, and Oppert, first deciphered the cuneiform script. In using the general term Babylonian Mathematics we must remember that the original and earlier Sumerian pictographic system, invented not later than the fourth millennium B.C., was modified by the later Babylonian scribes into a system of conventional characters on the introduction of their own Semitic language into the country. Babylonian mathematics is noteworthy for its positional principle by which the placing of numbers facilitated arithmetical computations.

Though subordinated to astrology, the patient observations of the heavenly bodies made over long periods of time by the Babylonian priesthood using primitive instruments, are a striking anticipation of the modern statistical method whereby a great number of values of the variables enable errors to be detected and laws discovered; for since all experimental observation involves selection, it is difficult to transcend a scheme of abstraction whose success is sufficiently wide.

The Old-Babylonian period is characterized by mathematical texts of *c.* 1700 B.C., which are cuneiform impressions made by a stylus upon clay, the Problem Texts of this period being collections of problems similar to those of school textbooks of today. There are also Table Texts which deal with the necessities of practical computation. The mathematical character of these texts and of later astronomical ones has rendered it easier to understand science as it was practised in Nippur, Kiš, and Nineveh. Sumerian-Babylonian numeration rests upon a sexagesimal system, a system which is still with us in the measurement of angles and the reckoning of time. On reaching 60 the symbol for unity was used again, but ambiguity was removed by the manner of placing of the figures, and the invention of further new symbols thus obviated. The Babylonian system of numeration, however, though it suggested the advantages to be gained by this relative place-value of the figures and also by their numerical monism (which removed symbolical distinctions between the orders of numbers such as decimals, units, tens, hundreds . . .), often remains ambiguous in practice when seen on the tablets which have come down to us, e.g. it is necessary to know the context of a statement to decide whether, say, a 2 occurring in it is to represent 2 or 20 or 200, or again perhaps 0;2 or 0;0,2. In order to interpret such texts Neugebauer introduces the comma and semicolon after the manner of the decimal system, e.g.

$$5,15 = (5 \times 60) + 15 = 315 \text{ in modern terms}$$

$$0;5 = \frac{5}{60} = \frac{1}{12}$$

$$0;0,5 = \frac{5}{60^2} = \frac{1}{720}$$

$$3,5,20,0 = 3(60^3) + 5(60^2) + 20(60) = 667,200.$$

The weakness of the system lies in this obscurity concerning absolute values and in the absence of a symbol for zero.

There were two phases in the early history of geometry, that of reckoning in terms of lines and that of reckoning in terms of angles. As far as evidence goes, both the Babylonians and Egyptians thought only in terms of lines, and the more difficult conception of the angle is due to the Greeks. Thus, the Babylonians knew that if an inclined beam, touching horizontal ground at its lower end and a vertical wall at its upper, is allowed to have any desired inclination, the relationship between the squares on the sides of the triangle thus formed is the one now known as the Theorem of Pythagoras, but they knew this simply as a relationship between lines and nothing more, and their knowledge no doubt arose as a result of the experiences gained by repeated practical measurement.

The Babylonians used their Table Texts in processes of multiplication and division, in operations involving the squares and cubes of numbers, and probably also in problems connected with the area and perimeter of a rectangle. In this last process their established facts, systematically tabulated, no doubt enabled them to solve the *particular* type of simultaneous equations written today as

$$a + b = p,$$
$$ab = q.$$

Given numerical values of the semi-perimeter p and the area q, the sides a and b of the rectangle might be found, not as we do today, but by simply tabulating solutions obtained by trial, and this information would be valuable in land-surveying in cases where a given area might be enclosed by different perimeters. Pursuing their expression of areas in terms of perimeters, the Babylonians also used $\frac{(\text{circumference})^2}{12}$* as the area of a circle. Finally, it is likely that the Table Texts were used in finding the sum, and the sum of the squares, of the natural numbers; for the Babylonians had rules for these sums.

Computation of ephemerides for the moon and planets may have been made in Babylonian astronomy as early as 1600 B.C., but the astronomy of the Seleucid Period, records of which go back to 800 B.C., reveals a computation of the new moons and the use of the lunar months in the civil calendar. The tablets of Enuma-Anu-Enlil and of Mul-Apin indicate the main development in the field of calendaric problems. The tablets of Mul-Apin deal with two specific methods of reckoning time, neither of which was supplanted until the discovery of the isochronism

* On writing circumference $= 2\pi r$ and area $= \pi r^2$ as in modern notation, and substituting the Babylonian value of $\pi = 3$, we obtain this approximate formula of the Babylonians.

of a simple pendulum by Galileo when a student at Pisa, 1581–5, and its elaboration in the clock by Huyghens in 1673 ; thus we read of the use of the sundial (later called gnomon by the Greeks) in estimating changes in the length of daylight throughout the seasons, and the relative measurement of time by the volumes or weights of water flowing from a regular prismatic clepsydra (or water-clock).

Assyrian learning of the seventh century B.C. is well represented by the large portion of the Royal Library of Ashur-bani-pal which remains to us. The chemical knowledge of the Assyrians was remarkable, e.g. they obtained liquid quicksilver by the roasting of solid cinnabar and were competent in the assaying of gold. We may indeed say that the origins of technical chemistry are Mesopotamian : the discovery at Ur in 1926 by Sir Leonard Woolley of the chemically-treated electrum spear-head *c.* 2700 B.C. bears striking witness.

During the period 300 B.C. to the beginning of the Christian era the later Babylonian astronomy was a highly-developed mathematical science, having a systematic theory of eclipses, and a lunar theory equalled only by the best contemporary Greek investigations.

(ii) EGYPT

Ancient Egypt has left us with many fascinating problems relating to the building of the Pyramids, the internal lighting of their chambers, the texture of the mummy-cloths, and the pigments which retain their colour unimpaired to the present day. For a record of the scientific achievements of the Ancient Egyptians reference must be made particularly to several famous papyri dating from the Middle and New Kingdoms, (*a*) the Medical Papyri named the Ebers (*c.* 1500 B.C.), the Hearst (*c.* 1400 B.C.), the Edwin Smith (*c.* 1600 B.C.), the Chester-

Beatty (*c.* 1250 B.C.), and the Kahūn (*c.* 1800 B.C.), and (*b*) the Ahmes Mathematical Papyrus (*c.* 2000 B.C.), forming a part of the Rhind collection in the British Museum. The last of these gives a good interpretation, as Egyptian mathematics had by that time become stabilized.

The Medical Papyri comprise works of real medical value together with recipes and entries of magical significance. The surgical texts relating to head and chest wounds to be found in the Edwin Smith Papyrus, those from the Ebers Papyrus concerning cysts, boils and carbuncles, and gynaecological entries in the Kahūn Papyrus, are all systematic in their approach to diagnosis and treatment. Their special significance seems to point to an earlier common source more rational than the body of magic with which they are recorded. The Edwin Smith Papyrus is perhaps the most important scientific document prior to Greek times. Of the valuable medical legacy bequeathed to later generations by the Egyptians may be mentioned their knowledge of comparative anatomy gained through the process of embalming the dead, their record of the symptoms and diagnosis of various stomach affections and female disorders, the recognition of the heart as the centre of the vascular system (though the function of the system was misunderstood), the recognition of localized functions in the brain (such as control of the limbs), and a valuable medical terminology ; further, the influence of Egyptian materia medica is to be found in the Hippocratic Collection, and in the later works of Pliny, Dioscorides, and Galen.

Systematic dissection of the human body by Greek anatomists and physicians was carried out in Alexandria in the time of Galen, and was a great stimulus to medical science, popular opinion in Egypt having been conditioned through centuries of past experience to such a procedure. The famous Greek historian Herodotus (fifth century B.C.) records the Greek debt to Egypt, and in medicine it was indeed great, Hippocratic medicine having its roots there. Egyptology has provided direct evidence of the effects of disease from the examination of mummies where the dates of death are accurately known.

Egyptian medicine, of which the scientific foundations were first laid five thousand years ago, was superior to and independent of that practised in Babylonia and Assyria: the latter had Sumerian origins and seems to have been transmitted mainly by oral tradition, for we are left only with concise summaries of diagnosis and prescriptions, and the Code of Hammurabi which regulated legally the work of the professional surgeons; whereas Babylonian mathematics was a new creation of the human spirit, Babylonian medicine remained largely a handmaid to religious and magical traditions.

The Egyptians made formal inscriptions in hieroglyphic, more cursive records on papyri in hieratic. In the hieratic and later demotic there are ciphered numerals. There was no positional principle as in the Babylonian cuneiform, and further symbols had to be invented for the higher numbers. Had the concise and tabular Egyptian cipherization been incorporated with the positional principle of the Babylonians, a system of numeration similar to our own would have emerged.

The four fundamental arithmetical rules were evolved in Egypt simply as methods of counting; e.g. the multiplication of 11 by 15, translated into modern terms, appears thus:

$$1 \times 11 = 11$$
$$2 \times 11 = 22$$
$$4 \times 11 = 44$$
$$8 \times 11 = 88$$

giving by addition $15 \times 11 = 165$

By successive doubling or halving, and by symbolic substitution of tens for units, hundreds for tens, and so forth, the usual calculations required in practical affairs were readily performed: beyond that the Egyptian did not generally seek to go. His practice of using fractions with unity as numerator (as for example $\frac{7}{12}$, written by him as $\frac{1}{3}\frac{1}{4}$) was cumbersome and restrictive. More difficult arithmetical problems were frequently solved by the method of *regula falsi*, in which an answer was obtained by supposition and the correct one obtained from it by simple proportion, e.g. Obtain a number, such that when it is increased by one-fifteenth, the result is 23.

Add $\frac{1}{15}$ to 15; the answer is 16. Divide 23 by 16 and multiply the result by 15. The result is $21\frac{9}{16}$, which was written in the form $21\frac{1}{2}\frac{1}{16}$. The method was frequently used by Diophantus of Alexandria in the third century A.D.

The Egyptians were thus able to solve "a simple equation" but not by algebra, and were also familiar with arithmetical and geometrical progressions, the area of the isosceles triangle and of the circle, and the volume of a right cylinder; but we must be very careful indeed not to invest their work with a degree of abstraction or a generality which it did not possess; in particular, though they probably used the calculation associated with the modern formula

$$\text{Area of a triangle} = \tfrac{1}{2} \times \text{base} \times \text{vertical height},$$

we are not certain whether it applied to *any* triangle; and further, their means of finding the area of a circle was a working rule, approximate, and giving a value of π of $\frac{256}{81}$ or 3·1605. With regard to Egyptian knowledge of the sides of the right-angled triangle Professor Sarton's remarks are pertinent:

it has been suggested that they were acquainted with the fact that a triangle whose sides were 3, 4 and 5 contained a right angle, and that they constructed right angles accordingly, as did the Chinese and the Indians. For this last statement I can find no foundation whatsoever: nothing in Egyptian mathematics suggests that the Egyptians were acquainted even with special cases of Pythagoras' theorem concerning the squares on the sides of a right-angled triangle.[1]

Two noteworthy features, however, do emerge from a consideration of the construction of the Pyramids: the method of reckoning slopes in terms of what is now called the cotangent of an angle, and the calculation of the volume of a truncated pyramid which surprisingly accords with the modern formula

$$\text{Volume} = \tfrac{1}{3}h(a^2 + ab + b^2),$$

where h is the vertical height and a and b the sides of the square sections forming the base and roof.

The technological achievements of the Ancient Egyptians have never ceased to cause wonder and admiration. Prototypes of the beam balance for weighing precious metals occurred as early as 2500 B.C. Their gold, however, usually contained silver which they could not separate. Metals had been both wrought and cast in the fourth millennium B.C., and by about 2000 B.C. they were able to use the harder bronze in place of copper. Papyrus sheets were probably made as early as 3000 B.C. Their main mechanical appliances used in building depended upon the principles of the lever, the inclined plane, the wheel or roller, the manometer, and the drill, and upon the geometrical instruments—the set-square, level, and plumb-line. It is significant that they did *not* use the grooved wheel or pulley. The Egyptians excelled in practical mensuration, but were definitely inferior to the Babylonians in notation, and in arithmetic and "algebra". It may be said that the Babylonians were intellectually the superior race, for this ascendency is to

[1] *Isis*, VI, p. 556, 1924.

be found in their language and their religion, resulting in a wider cultural influence upon the course of civilization as a whole: later Hebrew and Hindu geometry, for example, have a Babylonian origin.

There is ample evidence of astronomical activity in the Middle Kingdom, e.g. inscriptions on coffins at Ḥeny, and calendars on the coffin-lids from Asyut. Dekan calendars appear on coffin-lids as early as 2100 B.C. Dekans were groups of stars, or a single prominent star such as Sirius, which rose in the eastern heavens during successive periods of 10 days: thus there were 36 dekans, the twelve signs of the zodiac being unknown in early Egyptian astronomy. Star maps occur as early as 3500 B.C. and the dekanal system was certainly a feature of sacred lore by 2800 B.C. The geographical meridian could be obtained from the study of the shadow cast by a vertical rod at noon, and the positions of stars at night by a simple sighting instrument called the merkhet. The two earliest scientific instruments in existence are transit instruments; one belonged to Tutʿankhamūn, *c.* 1400 B.C., and was used to determine meridian time in order to set the water-clock.

It has been held that the greatest achievement of Egyptian science was the introduction of a practical calendar: indeed, the Julian calendar of 45 B.C. was the old Egyptian calendar of $365\frac{1}{4}$ days revived. As far as evidence goes, it appears that in the year 3141 B.C. the Egyptians instituted two calendars, of 365 and $365\frac{1}{4}$ days respectively, the latter gaining precedence.

Greek science was greatly stimulated by the technological achievements of Ancient Egypt, and many of the data it acquired from Egypt were to be used in framing the great generalizations which gave it pre-eminence: yet in spite of the Greek superiority Egyptian scientific practice and tradition died hard.

(iii) THE INDUS VALLEY, AND THE HINDU SUCCESSORS

Of the scientific achievements of the pre-Aryan civilization of the Indus Valley we as yet know little. It was roughly contemporary with the Sumerian civilization of which we have treated, was certainly very flourishing by 2300 B.C., and archaeological evidence proves without doubt that there was commercial intercourse between them. Excavations at Mohenjo-Daro in Sind and Harappā in the Punjab have revealed that

> in the third millennium before Christ, and even before that, the peoples of the Punjab and Sind were living in well-built cities and were in possession of a relatively mature culture with a high standard of art and craftsmanship and a developed system of pictographic writing.[1]

To this statement of Sir John Marshall, made in 1924, we can add only the brief, but highly significant, facts that this people used burnt bricks in their buildings, possessed an adequate system of street drainage, worked in copper and bronze (iron being unknown to them), and used weights.

It appears that the Vedic Aryan tribes entered North-West India during the second half of the second millennium B.C., and occupied the river valleys of the Indus, Ganges, and Jumna, thereby overrunning the domain of this earlier civilization. The culture of these Vedic Hindus has been preserved in their religious works from which occasional scientific achievements or observations can be inferred: for instance, a solar eclipse is mentioned in the Ṛgveda, but without clear evidence of date. The difficulty in estimating the scientific achievements of Ancient India lies in the absence of a reliable chronology: we can learn, however, something of its ideas through its Meru cosmology, no doubt suggested by the Himalayas, of which

[1] See *Revealing India's Past* (Roy. India Soc.), London, pp. 97–101.

brief mention will be made presently. For the moment, it may be noted that science was not entirely neglected during the periods of the great Hindu writings, namely, the Vedas and their supplementary Vedāngas, the later Saṃhitās, Brāhmaṇas, Āraṇyakas, and the Upanishads, the Sūtras, and the Purāṇas; and during the Greek influence spread by Alexander's campaign down the Indus (326–325 B.C.) and by the establishment of the Hellenic kingdoms of Syria, Bactria, and Parthia; nor in the Maurya Empire of Chandragupta, followed by the Buddhist expansion inspired by the Emperor Aśoka in the middle of the third century B.C. Amongst the earlier scientific achievements is the elaborate systematization of Sanskrit set forth in the grammar of Pānini and summarizing the efforts of many of his predecessors prior to the fourth century B.C.; the initiation of a treatise entitled *Kautilīya-Arthaśāstra* relating mainly to practical politics and ascribed to Kautilya, prime-minister to Chandragupta, at the end of the fourth century B.C.; the wonderful achievements of the Hindu medical schools of Ātreya and Suśruta; and the geometrical and arithmetical rules of Baudhāyana, Āpastamba, and Kātyāyana.

Ancient Hindu medicine and surgery are outstanding, and seem to have been carefully and systematically studied and practised as early as the sixth century B.C. According to the tradition in the Jātakas of the Buddhists:

> In the age of the Buddha there existed two great universities in India, Kāśī (or Benares) in the East and Takṣaśilā (or Taxila on the Jhelam river) in the West. Ātreya, the physician, taught in the latter university, and his younger contemporary, Suśruta, the surgeon, in the former.[1]

It was at Taxila that the scientists in Alexander's army first made contact with the Hindu sages, but to what extent Greek and

[1] Sarton, *Introduction to the History of Science*, I, 76.

Hindu science were mutually influential then or at any other time in antiquity is a controversial question which has not yet found an adequate answer. Suśruta was a true scientist, who combined direct observation with reliable theory. He describes several operations, e.g. relating to cataract, hernia, the caesarean section, plastic surgery; and gives an account of the surgical instruments used. Considerable information is recorded about anatomy, physiology, pathology, obstetrics, pediatrics, diagnosis, diet, and the plants used in medicine.

The mathematical achievements were less spectacular. They are to be found in the Śulva-sūtras (probably written between 400 and 200 B.C.), which are supplements to the Kalpa-sūtras dealing with the sacrificial altars required in the Vedic Hindu religious ceremonies. The term śulva-sūtra denotes "rules of the cord". These rules are, in effect, empirical formulae, arising from the problems of construction of altars, and are ancillary to religious ritual. They deal with the construction of squares and rectangles, the relation of the diagonals to the sides, equivalent squares and rectangles, and equivalent squares and circles. In the last connection, approximate formulae are given for converting a circle into a square of the same area, and vice versa. Many instances are recorded of the use of the Theorem of Pythagoras, though there appears to be no attempt to derive instances from a *general* rule; in fact, some of the formulae of the Śulva-sūtras, which seem on a first glance to suggest great mathematical possibilities, are found on closer analysis to be particular cases of an empirical nature and not the result of a systematic theory of geometry such as we find with the Greeks. Hindu mathematics has from time to time shown brilliant flashes of intuition by isolated geniuses, only to fail through lack of systematic development by their successors.

(iv) ANCIENT CHINA

Prior to about 500 B.C., the culture of the Chinese nation may be said to have flourished solely in the region of the Yellow River; indeed, until *c.* A.D. 1300, all the capitals of China were situated in a small area where the Yellow River emerges from the hills into the Great Plain, i.e. in the middle portion of its lower course. The Hsia Dynasty (*c.* 2205–1766 B.C.) is credited by tradition with irrigation, agriculture, writing, a calendar, and various technical arts. The Canon of Yao [1] "asserts that four named stars (Niao, Huo, Hsü, and Mao) mark the four tropic times, that the year is 366 days and that an intercalary moon is required to fix the seasons".[2] The four tropic times corresponded with the *middles* of the four seasonal quarters of the year, not with their beginnings as with the Greeks and with us. Much later, during the Han Dynasty (206 B.C.–A.D. 221), Niao, Huo, Hsü and Mao were identified with four of the 28 constellations of the equatorial belt of the heavens. According to De Saussure these 28 constellations are pre-Hsia, and may ante-date the Hindu *nakshatras*. In the later periods of the Chou Dynasty (1122–258 B.C.) there are accurate records of eclipses, and detailed star catalogues, and indications of still earlier uses of the gnomon and the clepsydra. It is not always clear when certain *mathematical* innovations were made in Ancient Chinese Astronomy, but the counting of days in tens (*hsün*), the sixty-day cycle, and the division of a year into twenty-four periods, were all in use by 600 B.C.

[1] Forms the first section of the Shu Ching (Classic of History). Its date of origin is still in dispute, but the general opinion is that it dates from the fourth century B.C.

[2] H. Chatley, *Ancient Chinese Astronomy*, p. 3. Reprint from the *Asiatic Review*, Jan. 1938. China Society, London.

The *Mo Ching* or Mohist Canons (late fourth century B.C.) contain interesting and penetrating observations on optics, relating especially to the action of the pinhole and to plane, concave, and convex mirrors. The inversion of the image produced by a pinhole camera was noted ; also the various forms of the image produced by a concave mirror when the object is moved gradually further away from it. When the concave mirror " faces the sun . . . the light is collected at a point as big as a hemp-seed, and when things touch this point fire is set up. This is the place where the ' waist ' is smallest ", Clearly the nature of the principal focus [1] had been understood. and the passage of a beam of light through it compared with the action of the pinhole camera. The observations made by the Chinese regarding images are superior to those of the contemporary Greek thought.

The Ancient Chinese had an elaborate technology in bronze ; they knew the proportions of copper and tin required to produce certain properties in the alloy ; and the white specular metal of the Han Dynasty, which contained below 32 per cent. of tin, was used in the making of excellent mirrors, which required no surfacing by silver or tin, and have remained underground for a thousand years without corrosion.

An interesting illustration of the Chinese practical sense occurs in their development of the breast-strap harness as early as 200 B.C. This harness came to Europe from China between A.D. 600 and A.D. 1000 and is the origin of the present-day

[1] When rays of light from the sun strike a concave mirror they are all reflected to a small region in front of the mirror which we name, in elementary optics, thep rincipal focus. The quotation is actually from Sher Kud, who wrote nearly 1500 years later [trans. J. Needham], but it merely crystallises Mohist ideas.

collar harness. It enabled a horse to draw heavier loads with greater ease; Europe had traditionally used the throat-and-girth harness of the Roman chariot, which showed a lack of knowledge of mechanics and of the horse.

Having dealt simply with the four River-Valley civilizations, we will now add to the general picture which we began to sketch at the beginning of this chapter. The cosmological conceptions of the Ancient Orient were those of the rectangular box of Egypt with the long sides north-south, or the Chinese cubical world, or again the pyramid, such as the hollow mountain of Nippur: in all cases they were based upon the 'square':

There is first of all the earth based on a square, with a corner towards the south, and shaped like a pyramid, with a number of successive homocentric square terraces rising up to a point (or rather, to a small square); on the top of this is the mount Meru, a pyramid widening out as it rises, at a small angle to the vertical; round this lie the orbits of the sun forming homologous squares on a horizontal plane; above the sun's plane is that of the moon with similar orbits. We may imagine that above this were the planes of the different planets at increasing heights, as described in the Visnu-purāna (of the Hindus); if these were also originally square orbits, we should have the original conception of the orbits of the planets as forming successive terraces of a pyramid representing the heavens.[1]

C. P. S. Menon goes on to suggest that the Pyramids of Egypt and the "towers" of Hindu temples may be models of the heavens.

This Meru cosmology was gradually modified by conceptions involving the circle: for example, in the *Sūryaprajñapti* of the

[1] Menon, *Ancient Astronomy and Cosmology*, p. 94.

Jains, possibly pre-Christian in date, though the century of composition is very uncertain, the universe consisted of flat concentric *rings* of land and sea, the central island or earth having at its own centre the mount Meru, around which the celestial bodies moved. The annual change of altitude of the sun (the obliquity of the ecliptic) was accounted for by the contraction and expansion of its orbit in a given plane, hence the winter solstice occurred when the orbit was largest and the sun had the least *apparent* altitude. In the *Sūryaprajñapti* there are estimates of the sizes of the celestial bodies, the orbits of the sun and moon, and the heights of orbits, the scheme being based upon shadow measurements involving determinations of the obliquity of the ecliptic and the latitudes of places. By making the orbits circular rather than square, a value of $\pi = \sqrt{10}$ was found.

The seventh and sixth centuries before Christ were characterized by a great awakening of the human spirit. Men were attempting to build a more satisfying explanation of the universe and of their own part in it. In the West it took the form of Greek rationalism, beginning with the Ionian School of Thales. Thales was able, on the basis of Babylonian data, to predict a solar eclipse on 28th May, 585 B.C., and many of the early Greek thinkers came under Asian influences. Indeed, in the time of Thales the peoples of the Eastern Mediterranean had a common fund of astronomical knowledge. With the first Hebrew prophets, such as 'Amōṣ, and with Zarathustra (Zoroaster) in Persia, came monotheism, which may be regarded as a scientific hypothesis. The distinction between the two kinds of outlook was later made clear by St. Paul: [1] "For the Jews require a sign and the Greeks seek after wisdom."

Then came the Buddha, Mahāvīra—the founder of Jainism,

[1] Corinthians i, 22.

Confucius—whose ideas were primarily ethical, and later Chuang-Tzŭ—the chief expounder of the Taoist philosophy. The teachings of the first and last of these are of particular interest in relation to the philosophy of science. The Order in Nature which the faith of the scientist compels him to assume is not unlike the Way of the Taoist. Further, the operation of this Order is by the Law of Causation, or Cause and Effect, namely, that if an event B follow an event A under certain conditions, then a repetition of event A on any further occasion under identical conditions will give rise again to event B. Hume, the eighteenth-century philosopher, held that the causal nexus is supplied by man himself in his attempt to reduce to order the bewildering flux of transient phenomena in the physical world, but without entering here into this and other philosophical difficulties connected with Causation, we may state simply that Causation which is regarded as valid in the material world by the scientist is extended by the Buddhist philosophy of *dhamma* to the whole of creation.

CAUSATION

The conviction of the unity of the order in nature is expressed in the book *Chuang-Tzŭ* (*c.* 300 B.C.) of the Taoist School: here Tung Kuo Tzu asks Chuang-Tzŭ: "Where is the so-called Tao?" and Chuang-Tzŭ replies: "Everywhere . . .

"You should not specify any particular thing. There is not a single thing without Tao. There are three terms: complete, all-embracing, and the whole. These three names are different, but denote the same reality—all refer to the one thing."

The Taoists were seeking to understand nature, and stood upon the threshold of both science and religion. Their mystical Way is to be studied in the *Tao Tê Ching*, attributed to the mythical Lao Tzŭ, but probably written in the third century B.C. In the *Tao Tê Ching* is mentioned the five 'element' theory in relation to sense impressions, e.g. to colours (blue, yellow, red, white, and black), to five musical tones, and to five tastes. This theory is also to be found in ancient Chinese astronomy in its division of the heavens into a central polar region and four peripheral regions. The Taoists also propounded a rudimentary doctrine of evolution and were the first alchemists, but their hypotheses were never *systematically* tested by experiment and so they never became true scientists.

The first known reference to alchemy in any language refers to the year 133 B.C. when the Emperor Han Wu-Ti after consultation with the alchemist Li Shao-Chün "who knew how to sacrifice to the stove", "also occupied himself in converting the cinnabar powder and other drugs into yellow gold". This reference occurs in the *Ch'ien Han Shu*,[1] written by Pan Ku in the first century A.D. The earliest known book dealing specifically with alchemy is the *Ts'an T'ung Ch'i* (*Unification of the Three Principles*) written by Wei Po-Yang about A.D. 140; an extract is worth quoting: [2]

> On the sides [of the apparatus] there is the walled enclosure, shaped like a pêng-hu pot. Closed on all sides, its interior is made up of intercommunicating labyrinths. The protection is so complete as to turn back all that is devilish or undesirable, and the meandering passages take good care of emergencies . . .
>
> In order that the treatise on fire shall not have been in vain, I shall explain here in simple language. Like the moon lying on its back is the shape of the furnace and the pot. In it is heated the White Tiger [Mercury]. Mercury Sun is the flowing pearl, and with it is the Blue Dragon. The east and west merge together, and the hun and po [two kinds of souls] control one another . . . The Red Bird is the spirit of fire and dispenses a victory or defeat with justice. With the ascending of water comes the vanquishing of fire . . .

---

[1] *History of the Earlier Han Dynasty.*

[2] Trans. Wu Lu-Chiang and T. L. Davis. *Isis,* XVIII, p. 210, 1932.

Treatment and mixing will bring about combination and rapid entrance to the scarlet portal. The escape must be firmly blocked. Below plays the dazzling flame, while the Dragon and the Tiger keep up a sustained vociferation. The flame at the start should be weak so as to be controllable, and should be made strong at the end. Close attention and careful watch should be given so as to regulate properly the heat and cold . . . The colour changes into a purple. Behold, the Returned Medicine is obtained. This is then made into pills. These are extremely efficacious, although their individual size is so small that they occupy only the point of a knife or the edge of a spatula . . .

Above, cooking and distillation take place in the cauldron ; below blazes the roaring fire. The White Tiger goes before, leading the way ; following comes the Grey Dragon [probably Sulphur]. The fluttering Scarlet Bird flies the five colours. Encountering snaring nets, it is helplessly and immovably pressed down and cries pathetically like a child after its mother. But irrevocably it is put down into the cauldron of hot fluid to the detriment of its feathers. Before half of the time has passed, Dragons appear with rapidity and in great number. The five dazzling colours change incessantly. Turbulently boils the fluid in the furnace. One after another they appear to form an array as irregular as a dog's teeth. Stalagmites, which are like mid-winter icicles, are split out horizontally and vertically. Rocky heights of no apparent regularity make their appearance, supporting one another. When Yin and Yang are properly matched, tranquillity prevails. [Yin and Yang, the male and female, positive and negative, attributes in the world.]

For the operation of the Order in Nature we may refer to the Pităkăs, the traditional Pāli writings of Buddhist Ceylon : here the process of the universe is defined in terms of *ñyāya* (system) and *dhamma* (cause). Cause, or Causation, is extended to both living and non-living matter in the generalization of *karma*. But it would be erroneous to push the analogy too far. The Buddha concerned himself primarily with moral law and escape from the wheel of illusion and suffering. The picture of existence as a transient world of physical phenomena in which all is *māyā* could not fail to direct attention away from experimental science.[1]

[1] See J. Needham: *Natural Law in China and in Europe.* Reprint. *Journal of History of Ideas*, Vol. XII, Nos. 1 and 2, 1951, p. 222.

2. *MEDIAEVAL CHINA*

Our knowledge of science in mediaeval China is still very inadequate, but active research into this subject is going on and it is hoped that a fuller picture of events may soon be perceived. Scientific progress in China was not delayed so effectively by Confucianism as it was in Europe by the rise of Christianity, and since Taoism was not unfavourable, there was sufficient interest to carry forward and develop the ideas of Antiquity. This led to certain remarkable technical achievements, such as the manufacture of paper and of gunpowder, and the invention of block-printing and of (possibly) the magnetic compass, though in this last instance the Muslim sailors may actually have adapted it for navigational purposes. The first of these occurred so early that it anticipated our mediaeval period, but we shall mention it here for the sake of convenience.

In the first year of the Yüan-Hsing period (A.D. 105), paper was made by Ts'ai Lun, an inspector of public works, from tree-bark, hemp, rags, and fish-nets; in the biographical section of the book *Hou Han Shu* (*History of the Later Han Dynasty*) written by Fan Yeh in the fifth century A.D., it was stated that henceforward paper was in general use and was called "the paper of Marquis Ts'ai". Pure rag paper of *c.* 150 A.D. has been found in a spur of the Great Wall of China by the famous Central Asian explorer and archaeologist, Sir Aurel Stein.

The Chinese were not lacking in appreciating the economic uses of the plant and animal kingdoms. The earliest description of the banana (*pa-chiao* plant) was written at the end of the second century A.D. in the book *I Wu Chih* (*Records of Strange Things*) by Yang Fu. Caravans carried Chinese silk to the West in Roman times, and the true mulberry silkworm was introduced from Khotan in A.D. 552 in the reign of Justinian. The Chinese author Lu Yü (late eighth century) was the first to produce a treatise on tea, *Ch'a Ching*, and in the late twelfth century Han Yen-Chih wrote the first work on citrous fruits, a comprehensive study of oranges and their cultivation.

Alchemy continued to flourish in both East and West. Between A.D. 317 and 332 a work, *Pao-p'o Tzu*, was written by Ko Hung. It deals with the theory and practice of early Chinese alchemy, and amongst many remarks which are in no way scientific we do find illuminating passages showing that the scientific mind was groping its way forward :

> Indeed the diversity is boundless, and some things which appear different are in fact the same. Sweeping laws should not be formulated too soon . . . If a generalization is driven too far it always ends in error, . . . If you drink an extract of hair and skin it will not cure your baldness.

Although alchemical theory frequently ended in verbal nonsense, the practical handling of substances produced useful discoveries such as that of real black ink (" indian ink ") from lampblack in the fourth or fifth century, and red ink from mercury sulphide (cinnabar) at a much earlier date. It is interesting to note that the Egyptians used both of these before the Chinese, and the discoveries seem to have been made independently.

A great civilizing influence came with the journeys of the Buddhist pilgrims from China to India, the fount of the wisdom of Gautama. As Professor Sarton has rightly said :

> The main point to emphasize is that the diffusion of Buddhism had for central and eastern Asia the same tremendous significance as the diffusion of Christianity for Europe. In both cases religion was the

vehicle of a higher civilization ; and, however much these two religions may have opposed or impeded the progress of science at later periods, we must not forget that it is they who made its birth possible and stimulated its first efforts in many and vast regions of the world. It is literally true that Christianity and Buddhism brought light and science with them, whenever they penetrated uncivilized countries.[1]

Buddhism came to Japan in 552, and Chinese culture and science followed in its wake, e.g. balances for weighing and tiles for the roofing of temples were introduced *c.* 590. The travels of Fa-Hsien of Shensi (early fifth century), Sung Yün of Tun-huang (early sixth century), Hsüan-Tsang of Honan (596–664), I-Ching (635–713), and others in search of the Buddhist scriptures make fascinating reading and are a source of valuable information on many subjects.

The Chinese excelled in mathematics, and particularly during this period of the Buddhist travellers mathematical ideas were exchanged between India and China, as we have already noted, so that it is not easy to make definite claims of priority in connection with certain discoveries, e.g. in the solution of indeterminate equations. The earliest indication of the abacus arithmetic, called in China *suan-p'an*, seems to occur in the work of Hsü Yo, who is said to have lived *c.* A.D. 150–200. Much Chinese arithmetic had originated from the classic treatise of Chang Ts'ang (d. 152 B.C.) entitled *Chiu Chang Suan Shu* (*The Arithmetical Rules in Nine Sections*), in which there is the earliest known mention of the negative quantity (*fu*), and this tradition was maintained through several centuries, being noticeable in the Arithmetical Classic of Hsia-Hou Yang (sixth century A.D.). In the second century A.D., however, the solution of indeterminate equations of the first degree, and a decimal system, appear in the work of Sun-Tzu ; an elaborate treatment of fractions

[1] *Introduction to the History of Science*, I, 470.

and further work on indeterminate equations occur in the Arithmetical Classic of Chang Ch'iu-chien (latter half of sixth century); and by the early seventh century Wang Hsiao-t'ung had solved simple cubic equations in connection with the volumes of solids, to be followed by further contributions to the study of indeterminate equations by I-hsing (683–727); so that the body of knowledge in the *Chiu Chang Suan Shu* was gradually augmented. The *Catalogue of the Sui Dynasty*, completed in 656, mentions many Hindu works on mathematics and astronomy, and there was a Chinese Astronomical Board from the seventh century onwards which had Hindu members; also the astronomical compendium, *Ta T'ang K'ai-Yüan Chan Ching* by Ch'ü-t'an Hsi-ta (eighth century), contains the Hindu decimal system derived from the Sanskrit; perhaps, then, ideas from Hindu mathematics were also absorbed. Yoshio Mikami, however, does not find any positive evidence for this transfer, and suggests that any transfer of knowledge which *might* have occurred would have been one from China to India. However, with our present evidence the question is an open one.

Medical studies were maintained by Chang Chung-ching, 'the Chinese Galen', who wrote at the end of the second century two treatises, one on dietetics and the other on fevers, both of which subsequently had considerable influence in Japan; by the surgeon Hua T'o, who flourished in the third century, and produced general anaesthesia by the use of a wine called *ma-fei-san* or *ma-yao*, of which we do not now know the composition; by the physician Ch'ao Yüan-fang (early seventh century), who wrote a treatise dealing with many diseases, including those of the eye, genito-urinary complaints, scabies, and impetigo contagiosa; by the T'ang emperor Kao Tsung (latter half of seventh century), who ordered the revision of the illustrated Chinese materia medica (*Pên Ts'ao*) in fifty-two books; by

Wang Tao, the author of a great medical treatise, which included some veterinary information and appeared in 752; by P'ang An-Shih (late eleventh century), who wrote a treatise on fevers; by Ch'ên Tzu-Ming, author in 1237 of a work on female disorders; by Sung Tz'u, who flourished *c.* 1250 and compiled a unique treatise on forensic medicine entitled *Instructions to Coroners*, which preceded European works of that kind by three hundred years; by Wang Hao-ku, another contemporary, who is said to have developed the knowledge and theory of the pulse; by Hu Ssu-hui, dietician to the Emperor Wên-Ti *c.* 1330, who treated the two forms of beriberi by dietary methods; by Hua Shou, author in 1341 of a practical treatise on the blood-vessels; by Chu Tan-ch'i (1281–1358), who mentioned the use of chaulmoogra oil as a treatment for leprosy; and finally by Chou Wang Ting, fifth son of the first Ming emperor Hung Wu, a physician and botanist who cultivated an experimental garden and completed in 1406 a herbal entitled *Chiu Huang Pên Ts'ao*, illustrated by remarkable woodcuts. It is interesting to note that prophylactic inoculation of smallpox was practised in China in the eleventh century.

The period of the T'ang Dynasty (A.D. 618–907) in China was a brilliant one, especially in poetry; Chinese culture spread both eastwards and westwards, and during this period cartographer Chia Tan completed (801) his great "Map of China and of the barbaric countries within the seas", printed documents were used in China and Japan, and Japan established its own University of Nara in the early eighth century.

By the end of the tenth century A.D., gunpowder was well established as a propulsive agent in war weapons in China. The earliest references to its use in war occur in the *Wu Ching Tsung Yao* (*Compendium of the Military Art*) by Tsêng Kung-Liang and others (A.D. 1044), and in that part of the *Sung Shih* (history of the Sung Dynasty) describing events *c.* 1150. A formula for gunpowder of A.D. 1040 has come down to us. The first projector using bullets, the T'u Huo Ch'iang with bamboo barrel, was made in A.D. 1259, to be quickly followed by the use of metal. Gunpowder had been first used by the Chinese in the seventh century for fireworks; it was the Mongol invasions of Europe in 1235 and 1261 which brought it, in a more terrifying rôle, to the Western world.

References to the use of block-printing in China towards the end of the T'ang Dynasty occur in the *Chia Hsün Hsü* (*Family Instructions*) of Liu Pin (about A.D. 900) and the *Ts'ê Fu Yuan Kuei* (*Encyclopaedia*) of Wang Ch'in Jo and Yang I (A.D. 1005). The earliest extant printed book, however, is a Chinese version of the *Diamond Sūtra*, dated May 11th, 868, and is now in the British Museum. It was one of the 15,000 books discovered by Sir Aurel Stein in 1907 in the caves of the Thousand Buddhas at Tun-huang, Kansu. This book is obviously the result of a long experience in block-printing, and so the art originated much earlier still. During the period Ching-Li (A.D. 1041–49) movable-type printing was first practised, as we learn from the *Mêng Ch'i Pi T'an* (*Essays of the Dream Pool*) written in the eleventh century by Shên Kua:

Pi Shêng, "a man in common cloth" (i.e. of the common people) "took sticky clay and cut in it characters as thin as the edge of a copper coin. Each character formed as it were a single type. He baked them in the fire to make them hard. He had previously prepared an iron plate covered with a mixture of pine resin, wax, and paper ashes. When he wished to print, he took an iron frame and set it on the iron plate. In this he placed the type, set close together. When the frame was full, the whole made one solid block of type. He then placed it near the fire to warm it. When the glue was slightly melted, he took a perfectly smooth board and pressed it over the surface so that the block of type became as even as a whetstone." . . . "As a rule, he kept two frames going. While the impression was being made from one frame, the type were being put in place on the other. When the printing of the first was finished, the second was ready. In this way the two frames alternated and the printing was done with great rapidity."[1]

Type of burnt earthenware was sometimes replaced by type made of other materials, as in the early fourteenth century by tin, and in the early fifteenth century (in Korea) by bronze. Owing to the large number of Chinese characters block-printing survived in spite of movable type.

In the twelfth century, in the *Complete Works of Chu Hsi*, we find the first known recognition of the true nature of fossils, and also a statement of the cosmology of the Neo-Confucian school:

Heaven and Earth were first nothing but ch'i (pneuma) in its two forms, Yin and Yang (the two fundamental principles, dark and light, female and male, etc.). This pneuma or fluid was in motion, grinding this way and that so that by violent friction there resulted in the formation of a great quantity of sediments. There being no space in the centre to escape, they coagulated and formed a solid earth in the centre. The purest (particles of) fluid became the sky, the sun, the moon, and the stars, which are permanently revolving and turning round outside. The earth stayed in the centre motionless, though it could not be called "below". Heaven moved unrestingly, turning round by day and night. Thus earth was in its centre like a swimming bridge. Should Heaven stop only for one instant, earth must fall down. The gyration of the heavens was so fast that a great amount of sediment was amassed in the middle, and this is the earth. Therefore it is said that the purer and lighter parts become Heaven and the grosser and more turbid parts Earth.[2]

Fossils

---

[1] Trans. T. F. Carter. *The Invention of Printing in China and its spread Westwards* p. 160. New York, 1925.

[2] Trans. A. Forke. *The World Conception of the Chinese.* London, 1925.

But more important is the development of a golden age of Chinese mathematics. Of the several eminent mathematicians and astronomers of this age may be noted Ch'in Chiu-shao, who flourished *c.* 1250 and developed the theory of indeterminate equations on similar lines to that of the Hindu method of the multiplier (*kuṭṭaka*) ; Li Chih (Li Yeh) (*c.* 1178–1265), who dealt with trigonometrical measurements relating to the circle ; 'Īsā the Mongol (Ai-hsieh), a Nestorian who became director of the astronomical bureau of Kublai Khān in 1263 ; Cha-Ma-Lu-Ting (one Jamāl al-Dīn), a Persian astronomer who introduced Persian instruments to China and prepared a new calendar for Kublai Khān ; Kuo Shou-Ching (1231–1316), who constructed fine astronomical instruments, probably introduced Muslim spherical trigonometry into China, and also prepared a new calendar for Kublai Khān ; Yang Hui (flourished *c.* 1270), whose works involved arithmetical progressions, linear and quadratic equations, and the use of decimal fractions ; and finally, Chu Shih-chieh (flourished *c.* 1290), the famous mathematician whose algebra had a great influence in Japan, and who dealt with a system of linear equations having four unknown quantities, and with the summation of certain algebraic series.

When writing, Ch'in Chiu-shao used red and black inks to denote positive and negative quantities respectively, but Li Chih dispensed with colours and made diagonal lines across the negative quantities to distinguish them. The application of the use of red and black computing rods to algebraical problems by Ch'in Chiu-shao enabled him to solve difficult equations by a method which he called *t'ien yüan shu* (the method of the celestial element)—which later became known as *tengen jutsu* in Japan—and which was applied by Chu Shih-chieh, in his treatise of A.D. 1303 entitled *Ssŭ Yüan Yü Chien* (*The Precious Mirror of the Four Elements*), to the solution of the linear equations having four unknowns. The four unknowns or elements were *jen* (man), and *ti* (earth), *t'ien* (heaven), and *wu* (things or matter). This method of *t'ien yüan shu* (*tengen jutsu*) no doubt inspired the Japanese development of the theory of determinants (see Chapter 5).

The astronomical instruments of equatorial design built *c.* 1279 under the supervision of Kuo Shou-Ching at Pei-ping (Peking) for Kublai Khān represent perhaps the most advanced observational technique up to their time and anticipate Tycho Brahe in Europe by some two hundred years. Although Muslim scholars were held in esteem and helped to maintain Mongol astronomical studies between 1280 and 1368, the Mongol instruments extant exemplify their own division of the circle into $365\frac{1}{4}$ degrees, there being 100 minutes per degree, and 100 seconds per minute, and Dr. M. C. Johnson has drawn the following conclusion about them :

> The result suggests that just at the era of readiest availability of Western astronomical methods Kuo Shou-Ching deliberately set aside the latter and reverted to a technique which had already been in use in Chinese astronomy for twelve centuries. We have distinguished certain features in which the Chinese methods were inferior to the contemporary Persian, and other features more close to present-day practice and antedating by 400 years the introduction of the latter from Europe. The surviving instruments of 1279 must therefore be accepted as quite independent of the great Moslem scientific age.[1]

Dr. Joseph Needham's remarks are of interest :

> Fortunately we do still possess some of the contemporary astronomical instruments made during the Yüan dynasty in China under the supervision of Kuo Shou-ching in 1279, for the observatory which still exists at the south-east corner of the Tartar city-wall at Pekin. I myself have had the good luck to visit this holy place of science, though it now

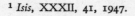

[1] *Isis*, XXXII, 41, 1947.

contains only the Jesuit instruments of the 17th century, the Mongol ones having been removed to the Purple Mountain at Nanking.[1]

Chinese engineers had from the earliest times paid attention to rivers and canals, and books had been written on their conservancy. The Grand Canal which linked the old Sung capital of Hangchow with the Yellow River was extended under the direction of Kublai Khān from the Yellow River to his own newly-built capital of Khānbaliq (on the site of the present Peking), thus completing a continuous waterway of 1,200 miles. Two treatises concerning the Yellow River or Huang-Ho were written during this Yüan (Mongol) Dynasty (1280–1368), namely, the *Ho fang t'ung i* by Sha-K'o-shih and the *Chih ho t'u lüeh* by Wang Hsi.

It is difficult as yet to say precisely what debt the West owes to China for her technical inventions, but it is a very big one, e.g. the seventh century A.D. saw paddle-wheel propulsion of boats in China. Chinese applied science or technology has progressed, perhaps very slowly, over the centuries, but it has gone forward all the time, and

> technical inventions show a slow but massive infiltration from east to west throughout the Christian era.[2]

> . . . all we can say is that in spite of Vitruvius and the previous theorists Philo and Ctesibius, Asia was greatly in advance of Europe (in technology) from the earliest times until about the sixteenth century. We always have to bear in mind that inventions may have been made in Central Asia, about the history of which comparatively little is known, and spread in both directions.[3]

In any case, China took her full share in these developments.

[1] *The Unity of Science: Asia's Indispensable Contribution*, Archives Internat. d'Hist. des Sciences, II, 566, 1949.

[2] *Op. cit.*, p. 4.

[3] *Op. cit.*, p. 15.

3. MEDIAEVAL INDIA

THE astronomical and mathematical achievements of mediaeval India exhibit some striking discoveries in certain limited fields of knowledge but not in others ; in general, the results suffered from isolation and lack of systematic development by a succession of workers. The Siddhāntas[1] contain the main features of Hindu astronomy, and at the time of Varāhamihira, c. A.D. 550, who summarized them in his *Pañchasiddhāntikā*, there were five such treatises, viz. the *Paitāmaha*, *Vāsishṭha*, *Romaka*, *Pauliśa*, and *Sūrya Siddhāntas*. According to G. R. Kaye, the Hindus were then remodelling their astronomy on Greek ideas, incorporating some of their technical terms, Greek names for the signs of the zodiac, and the seven-day week. Whereas the *Paitāmaha Siddhānta* retains the Vedāṅga astronomy, the *Vāsishṭha Siddhānta* represents the transitional stage, and the last-named three show unmistakable signs of Greek influence, as for example in the *Romaka Siddhānta*, where the year of 365 days 5 hours 55 minutes 12 seconds is exactly the tropical year of Hipparchus. The words of Al-Bīrūnī are of interest :

The science of astronomy is the most famous among them, since the affairs of their religion are in various ways connected with it. If a man wants to gain the title of an astronomer, he must not only know scientific or mathematical astronomy, but also astrology. The book known among Muslims as *Sindhind* is called by them Siddhânta, i.e. *straight*, not crooked nor changing. By this name they call every standard book on astronomy, even such books as, according to our opinion, do not come up to the mark of our so-called Zīj, i.e. handbooks of mathematical astronomy. They have five Siddhântas :

---

[1] Siddhānta, *lit.* established conclusion.

I. *Sûrya-siddhânta*, i.e. the Siddhânta of the sun, composed by Lâta.

II. *Vasishṭha-siddhânta*, so-called from one of the stars of the Great Bear, composed by Vishṇucandra.

III. *Pulisa-siddhânta*, so-called from Paulisa, the Greek, from the city of Saintra, which I suppose to be Alexandria, composed by Pulisa.

IV. *Romaka-siddhânta*, so-called from the Rûm, i.e. the subjects of the Roman Empire, composed by Śrîsheṇa.

V. *Brahma-siddhânta*,[1] so called from Brahman, composed by Brahma-gupta,t he son of Jishṇu, from the town of Bhillamâla between Multân and Anhilwâra, 16 yojana from the latter place.

The authors of these books draw from one and the same source, the Book of Paithâmaha, so called from *the first father*, i.e. Brahman:[2]

The *Paitāmaha Siddhānta* incorporates information going back to A.D. 80.

Hindu astronomy was largely determined by the *Sūrya Siddhānta*, which probably uses material originating as early as A.D. 400, but which dates in its present text from about A.D. 1000. Prabodhchandra C. Sengupta writes:[3]

. . . from 100 to 400 A.D. we have a great gap of three hundred years in which astronomical knowledge from Babylonia and Greece came to India. The oldest Sūrya Siddhānta, was transmitted to this country during this period and its astronomy was most probably of a little

[1] Al-Bīrūnī is referring to the Brahma-sphuṭa-Siddhānta, which Brahmagupta composed on the basis of the earlier Brahma-Siddhānta (sphuṭa, corrected). This earlier treatise formed part of the Vishnu-dharmottara Purāna, which professed to be a divine revelation.

[2] E. Sachau, *Alberuni's India*, I, 152.

[3] The following quotations are from the edition of Gangooly and Sengupta (see Select Bibliography).

more improved type than that of the Vasiṣtha Siddhānta of the Pañca Siddhāntikā.[1]

We accordingly conclude that the earliest date of the Sūrya Siddhānta cannot be pushed up much higher than A.D. 400, while A.D. 499 was the date of our most famous astronomer Āryabhaṭa I.

Sengupta goes on to refute the statement of Al-Bīrūnī that Lāṭa composed the *Sūrya Siddhānta* :

. . . Alberūnī has said in his Indika that the Sūrya Siddhānta was composed by Lāṭadeva. We now know that Lāṭa, the expounder of the Romaka and the Pauliśa Siddhāntas according to Varāhamihira, was a direct pupil of Āryabhaṭa I and got the appellation of

SARVASIDDHANTAGURU

the teacher of all the systems of Siddhāntas. . . . Suffice it to say that it has had a composite growth, . . . It took its present form decidedly after the time of Brahmagupta. The earliest person by whom its constants and methods were changed was no doubt Varāhamihira, the changes effected were certainly taken from Āryabhata I's āndharātrika or 'midnight' system.

The *Sūrya Siddhānta* deals with (I) the mean motions of the planets, (II) the true positions of the planets, (III) direction, place, and time, (IV)–(VI) the treatment of eclipses, (VII) planetary conjunctions, (VIII) asterisms, (IX) heliacal risings and settings, (X) the rising and setting of the moon, (XI) "certain malignant aspects of the sun and moon", (XII) cosmogony, geography, and the "dimensions of the Creation", (XIII) measuring instruments, including the armillary sphere, clepsydra, and gnomon, (XIV) the different ways of reckoning time ; and there is also much astrology in it.

[1] P. C. Sengupta, "Āryabhaṭa," *Cal. Univ. Journal of Letters,* Vol. XVIII, pp. 9–15.

The earth is regarded as a stationary sphere around which the heavenly bodies revolve :

Twice eight hundred *yojanas* are the diameter of the earth : the square root of ten times the square of that is the earth's circumference. This, multiplied by the sine of the co-latitude (*lambajyâ*) of any place, and divided by radius (*trijîvâ*) is the corrected (*sphuṭa*) circumference of the earth at that place.

The distance of the moon was taken as 51,570 *yojanas*, i.e.

$$\frac{\text{distance of moon from earth}}{\text{diameter of earth}} = 30\tfrac{7}{12},$$

roughly the result of Ptolemy. Planetary distances are calculated by assuming that planetary velocities are all equal, and the paths of the planets worked out on the epicyclic theory, as was used earlier by the Greeks. The obliquity of the ecliptic was given as 24°, and the precession of the equinoxes considered to be a motion of 54 seconds per year within the limits 27° east and west of a fixed position. The prime meridian of longitude was taken through Avantī, or Ujjayinī—the ancient city of Hindu culture and astronomy (modern Ujjain[1]) described in the *Meghaduta* (*Cloud-Messenger*) of the poet Kālīdāsa.

Anthropomorphism was introduced to account for the mechanism of planetary motion ; indeed, the search for some kind of prime mover in the universe was general until the researches of Galileo and Newton in the seventeenth century led to the establishment of centrifugal force and gravitational attraction on a mathematical basis.

Forms of Time, of invisible shape, stationed in the zodiac (*bhagaṇa*), called the conjunction (*çīghrocca*), apsis (*mandocca*), and node (*pâta*), are causes of the motion of the planets.

The planets, attached to these beings by cords of air, are drawn away

[1] On the Upper Chambal River.

by them, with the right and left hand, forward or backward, according nearness, toward their own place.

A wind, moreover, called provector (*pravaha*) impels them toward their own apices (*ucca*) ; being drawn away forward and backward, they proceed by a varying motion. . . .

As in the *Pauliśa Siddhānta*, we are introduced to trigonometry : the *Sūrya Siddhānta* treats both of sines (*jyā*) and versed sines (*utkramajyā*), though the Hindus did not conceive of the cosine in the way that we do. There is also an interesting description of the Hindu gnomon and dial :

On a stony surface, made water-level, or upon hard plaster, made level, there draw an even circle, of a radius equal to any required number of the digits (*angula*) of the gnomon (*çanku*).

At its centre set up the gnomon, of twelve digits [1] of the measure fixed upon ; and where the extremity of its shadow touches the circle in the former and after parts of the day,

There fixing two points upon the circle, and calling them the forenoon and afternoon points, draw midway between them, by means of a fish-figure (*timi*), a north and south line.

Midway between the north and south directions draw, by a fish-figure, an east and west line : and in like manner also, by fish-figures (*matsya*) between the four cardinal directions, draw the intermediate directions.

Draw a circumscribing square, by means of the lines going out from the centre ; by the digits of its base-line (*bhujasûtra*) projected upon that is any given shadow reckoned.

This is immediately followed by a mathematical discussion on the right-angled triangle formed by the gnomon, its shadow, and the hypotenuse, and on the path of the shadow in the plane of the dial. Thus, for instance, the sine of the sun's altitude

[1] About 9 inches in all.

is represented by the gnomon and called *çanku* (" staff ")when the hypotenuse joining tip of shadow and tip of gnomon is regarded as a radius. The Hindus reckoned essentially in terms of lines, or boundaries, and sines, and seldom used the term " angle " (*koṇa*), which seems to have been borrowed from the Greek *γωνια*.

The gnomon and the clepsydra seem to have been the only two instruments regularly used : there is a description of the armillary sphere, but apparently only for demonstration purposes. The clepsydra for measuring time is described thus : " A copper vessel, with a hole in the bottom, set in a basin of pure water, sinks sixty times in a day and night, and is an accurate hemispherical instrument." The sixtieth part of a day, *ghaṭi* or *ghaṭikā* (*lit.* vessel), seems to be derived from it. The vessel

is to be of ten *palas*' weight of copper, six digits (*angula*) high, and of twice that width at the mouth, and is to contain sixty *palas* of water : the hole in the bottom through which it is to fill itself is to be such as will just admit a gold pin four digits long, and weighing three and a half *mâshas*.

Authorities have differed respecting the origin of the Hindu astronomy. Whitney in 1860 wrote :

We regard the Hindu science as an offshoot from the Greek, planted not far from the commencement of the Christian era, and attaining its fully developed form in the course of the fifth and sixth centuries. . . . The absence from the Hindu system of any of the improvements introduced by Ptolemy into that of the Greeks tends strongly to prove that the transmission of the principal groundwork of the former took place before his time : . . . It is, in our own view, altogether likely that the science came in connection with the lively commerce which, during the first centuries of our era, was carried on by sea between Alexandria, as the port and mart of Rome, and the western coast of India, *not* " overland through the Syrian, Persian, and Bactrian kingdoms which stood under Greek government, . . ." [1]

G. R. Kaye, writing more recently, has also given great weight to Greek influence, but has suggested precisely those routes which Whitney ignored :

> Other possible paths of communication between the Indians and Greeks are by way of China and by way of Persia. The former is not so improbable as it at first seems. Further information about the early silk trade with China might possibly throw light on the subject. The intellectual communication between India and China at the critical period is well known—there being numerous references to such communication in Chinese literature. If sound translations of the early Chinese mathematical works were available, we might be able to draw more definite conclusions, but as the evidence now stands there is nothing that would warrant more than the bare suggestion of a Chinese source.
>
> We have already mentioned the visit of certain Greek mathematicians to the Court of Chosroes I, and there are certain other facts which at least justify the consideration of the Persian route. The Sássánid period, A.D. 229–652, shows a somewhat remarkable parallelism with the age of enlightenment in India that roughly corresponds with the Gupta period. " The real missionaries of culture in the Persian empire at this time were the Syrians, who were connected with the west by their religion and who, in their translations, diffused Greek literature throughout the orient." Mr. Vincent Smith discusses the probability of Sassanian influence on India but states that there is no direct evidence.
>
> Although it may be possible to offer only conjectures as to actual route by which any particular class of Greek knowledge reached India, the fact remains that during the period under consideration the intellectual influence of Greek on India was considerable. It is evident not only in the mathematical work of the Indians but also in sculpture, architecture, coinage, astronomy, astrology, etc. Mr. Vincent Smith

[1] See edition of Gangooly and Sengupta, Appendix.

refers "to the cumulative proof that the remarkable intellectual and artistic output of the Gupta period was produced in large measure by reason of the contact between the civilization of India and that of the Roman Empire"; and research is almost daily adding to such proof.

The flourishing state of the Gupta Empire, the greatest in India since the days of Asoka, and the wise influence of its principal rulers, gave a great impetus to scholarship of all kinds. The numerous embassies to and from foreign countries—which were means of intellectual as well as political communication—no doubt contributed to the same end; and the knowledge of Greek works displayed by Āryabhaṭa, Varāha Mihira, and Brahmagupta was one of the natural results of this renaissance of learning.[1]

There is, however, another side to the question. The Rev. E. Burgess, who lived in the Bombay Presidency from 1839 to 1854 as missionary to the Marāthas and made the standard English translation of the *Sūrya Siddhānta* "with the aid of Brahmans who were familiar with the Sanskrit and well versed in Hindu astronomical science", disagreed with the findings of Whitney:

I think he does not give the Hindus the credit due to them, and awards to the Greeks more credit than they are justly entitled to. In advancing this opinion, however, I admit that the Greeks, at a later period, were the more successful cultivators of astronomical science. There is nothing among the Hindu treatises that can compare with great Syntaxis [Almagest] of Ptolemy. And yet, from the light I now have, I must think the Hindus original in regard to most of the elementary facts and principles of astronomy as found in their systems, and for the most part also in their cultivation of the science; and that the Greeks borrowed from them, or from an intermediate secondary source, to which these facts and principles had come from India. I might perhaps so far modify this statement as to admit the supposition that neither Greeks nor Hindus borrowed the one from the other, but both from a

[1] G. R. Kaye, *Indian Mathematics*, p. 44 (1915).

common source. But with my present knowledge, I cannot concur in the opinion that the Hindus are, to any great extent, indebted to the Greeks for their astronomy, or that the latter have any well grounded claims to the honor of originality in regard to those elementary facts and principles of astronomical science which are common to their own and other ancient systems, and which are of such a nature as indicates for them, a common origin, and a transmission from one system to another.[1]

Without entering fully into the difficult question of priority and transference of this knowledge, enough has been said here to indicate the complexity of the problem and the lack of finality in our data concerning it : the uncertainty of Indian chronology renders a conclusion impossible at present. We *tend* to agree with W. E. Clark :

Even if the impetus toward a new astronomy was received by India from Greece by the acceptance of some general ideas, these were cleverly adapted to the older Indian cosmography and modes of reckoning. What had been borrowed was thoroughly Hinduized and completely assimilated into Indian culture.[2]

Perhaps most conspicuous amongst those general ideas were the theories of eccentrics and epicycles for planetary motion, of which the great Sanskrit scholar, H. T. Colebrooke, wrote with reserve in 1816, and which may have reached India around the time of Christ.

The distinguished Hindu astronomers, with the dates at which they flourished, are Āryabhaṭa I [3] (A.D. 499), his pupil Lāṭadeva (A.D. 505), Varāhamihira (A.D. 550), Brahmagupta (A.D. 628), Lalla (A.D. 748), Mañjula (A.D. 932), Śrīpati (A.D. 1028), and

[1] *Sūrya-Siddhānta*, edition of Gangooly and Sengupta.

[2] *Legacy of India* (Garratt), p. 351.

[3] A second Āryabhaṭa flourished sometime between Brahmagupta and Bhāskara.

Bhāskara II (A.D. 1150). As some of them also made significant contributions to mathematics we shall now proceed to discuss these.

The first Hindu algebraist was Āryabhaṭa I. His brief recorded work is embodied in thirty-three stanzas in his *Āryabhaṭīya*, an astronomical writing of A.D. 499. He defined algebra by the name *bīja*, and initiated a branch of it under the name *kuṭṭaka*, which involved the resolution of indeterminate equations of the first degree. More will be said presently about this latter development as it was peculiar to both India and China at this period. Āryabhaṭa's work included statements about interest, rule of three, fractions, square and cube roots, simple areas and volumes, the simpler properties of circles, gnomon problems and sines, arithmetical progressions, factors, and simple algebraic identities—the whole very much condensed and acting primarily as a criterion of the state of mathematical knowledge at that time. Whilst a very accurate value of $\pi = 3\frac{177}{1250}$ (i.e. 3·1416) is recorded (though not used), there are inaccurate formulae for the volumes of the sphere and pyramid.

The next mathematician of note was Brahmagupta, whose writings are set forth in the twelfth and eighteenth chapters of his astronomical treatise *Brahmasphuṭa-siddhānta*, composed in A.D. 628. He dealt especially with the diagonals and areas of cyclic quadrilaterals (i.e. four-sided figures with their angles on the circumference of a circle), and gave the following theorems, which are here stated in modern terms:

(1) If the sides of a cyclic quadrilateral are of lengths a, b, c, d, and its semi-perimeter is s, then its area is

$$A = \sqrt{s(s-a)(s-b)(s-c)(s-d)}$$

(2) If the diagonals of the same quadrilateral are of lengths x and y, then the relations between these diagonals and the

sides of the quadrilateral are expressed by " Brahmagupta's Theorem " :

$$x^2 = (ad + bc)(ac + bd) \div (ab + cd),$$
$$y^2 = (ab + cd)(ac + bd) \div (ad + bc).$$

(3) If a, b, c and α, β, γ are the sides of two separate right-angled triangles, such that $a^2 + b^2 = c^2$, and $\alpha^2 + \beta^2 = \gamma^2$, then if we make a quadrilateral of which the sides are the products $a\gamma$, $c\beta$, $b\gamma$, and $c\alpha$, then this quadrilateral, which has been called " Brahmagupta's Trapezium ", will be cyclic and have its diagonals at right-angles.

This more outstanding work of Brahmagupta was unfortunately underrated by his successors : for instance, Bhāskara said, " How can a person neither specifying one of the perpendiculars, nor either of the diagonals, ask the rest ? Such a questioner is a blundering devil and still more so is he who answers the question."

Brahmagupta also knew the rules for arithmetical operations involving zero, appreciated the use of negative quantities and of negative terms in algebra (which the Muslim algebraists later ignored), studied quadratic equations, and had considerable success in the solution of indeterminate equations of the second degree. He further stated a rule giving the radius r of the circle circumscribing a triangle ABC (of sides a, b, c) which we now express in the form

$$2r = \frac{a}{\sin \angle A} = \frac{b}{\sin \angle B} = \frac{c}{\sin \angle C}.$$

Mathematical writings are also to be found in the *Mahāsiddhānta* of Āryabhaṭa II, the *Gaṇitasārasamgraha* of Mahāvīra, and the *Gaṇitasāra* of Śrīdhara. Mahāvīra (*c.* A.D. 850) concerned himself especially with the right-angled triangle having the lengths of its sides in whole numbers, and with the area and circumference of the ellipse; but in the latter investigation his results were inaccurate. He also dealt with geometrical progressions. Śrīdhara (*c.* A.D. 1020) gave a general rule for the solution of quadratic equations.

The general appreciation of the development of Hindu mathematics is, however, best drawn from the *Līlāvatī* and *Bīja-Ganita* of Bhāskara, which are the arithmetical and algebraical sections of his astronomical treatise *Siddhānta-śiromani*. Bhāskara was born in A.D. 1114, and his treatise written *c.* 1150 forms a useful summary of the mediaeval period in Hindu mathematical thought. As with many mediaeval treatises, the book *Līlāvatī* opens [1] with invocations to the Deity, in this instance, the god Ganeśa:

> Having bowed to the deity, whose head is like an elephant's; whose feet are adored by gods; who, when called to mind, relieves his votaries from embarrassment; and bestows happiness on his worshippers; I propound this easy process of computation, delightful by its elegance, perspicuous with words concise, soft and correct, and pleasing to the learned.[2]
>
> Salutation to Ganeśa, resplendent as a blue and spotless lotus; and delighting in the tremulous motion of the dark serpent, which is perpetually twining within his throat.[3]

The examples, some of which are addressed to one Līlāvatī, are of considerable interest, e.g.:

> Beautiful and dear Līlāvatī, whose eyes are like a fawn's! tell me what are the numbers resulting from one hundred and thirty-five, taken into twelve? if thou be skilled in multiplication by whole or by parts, whether by subdivision of form or separation of digits. Tell me,

[1] Quotations are from Colebrooke's edition of 1817.
[2] Chapter I. [3] Chapter II, Section I.

auspicious woman, what is the quotient of the product divided by the same multiplier ?[1]

Out of a swarm of bees, one-fifth part settled on a blossom of cadamba ; and one-third on a flower of silínd'hrí ; three times the difference of those numbers flew to the bloom of a cutaja. One bee, which remained, hovered and flew about in the air, allured at the same moment by the pleasing fragrance of a jasmin and pandanus. Tell me, charming woman, the number of bees.[2]

In a certain lake swarming with ruddy geese and cranes, the tip of a bud of lotus was seen a span above the surface of the water. Forced by the wind, it gradually advanced, and was submerged at the distance of two cubits. Compute quickly, mathematician, the depth of the water.[3]

How many are the variations of form of the god Çambhu by the exchange of his ten attributes held reciprocally in his several hands : namely the rope, the elephant's hook, the serpent, the tabor, the skull, the trident, the bedstead, the dagger, the arrow, and the bow : as those of Hari by the exchange of the mace, the discus, the lotus, and the conch ?[4]

Since the arithmetic of apparent [or known] quantity which has been already propounded in a former treatise, is founded on that of unapparent [or unknown] quantity ; and since questions to be solved can hardly be understood by any, and not at all by such as have dull apprehensions, without the application of unapparent quantity ; therefore I now propound the operations of analysis.

Thus does Bhāskara pass from *Līlāvatī* to the wider generalization of *Bīja-Ganita.* "It is apparent to men of clear understanding, that the rule of three terms constitutes arithmetic ; and sagacity, algebra . . . spotless understanding is algebra." H. T. Colebrooke has commented aptly that

[1] Chapter II, § 16. On Logistics.
[2] Chapter III, § 54. On Supposition.
[3] Chapter VI, § 153. On Plane Figures.
[4] Chapter XIII, § 269. On Combination.

In a very general sense, the analytic art, as Hindu writers observe, is merely sagacity exercised; and is independent of symbols, which do not constitute the art. In a more restricted sense, according to them, it is calculation attended with the manifestation of its principles: and, as they further intimate, a method aided by devices, among which symbols and literal signs are conspicuous. Defined, as analysis is by an illustrious modern mathematician,[1] "a method of resolving mathematical problems by reducing them to equations", it is assuredly not to be found in the works of any Grecian writer extant, besides Diophantus.

The Hindus, however, went far beyond the work of Diophantus. *Bīja-Ganita* contains sections on notation or algorithm; cipher or zero and its use; unknown quantities; surds; the pulverizer or *kuṭṭaka* (also dealt with in *Līlāvatī*); simple and quadratic equations, including a general rule for the solution of the latter which went beyond that of Śrīdhara; solutions of several indeterminate equations of the second degree; and solutions of certain equations of the third and fourth degree.

It is now convenient to summarize briefly the unique Hindu achievements in (1) the solution of indeterminate equations, (2) arithmetical and algebraic notation and the decimal system, (3) the origin of trigonometry.

(1)

During the fourth century A.D. and succeeding centuries of the mediaeval period there was considerable interchange of ideas between India and China; especially did learned Chinese travel to India in search of the Buddhist scriptures. It seems possible that the Hindu interest in indeterminate equations was inspired, just as the Japanese development of determinant algebra was inspired later, by Chinese work in the same field.

[1] D'Alembert.

We do not yet know enough about the history of science in China to be emphatic, but examples of indeterminate equations of the first degree occur in the treatise *Sun Tzu Suan Ching* of the second century A.D., and are followed by similar ones in the works of Brahmagupta and Mahāvīra. By the latter half of the sixth century A.D. we encounter the famous Problem of One Hundred Fowls in the Chinese treatise *Chang Ch'iu-Chien Suan Ching* :

A cock costs five pieces of money, a hen three pieces, and three chickens together one piece. If we buy with one hundred pieces, one hundred fowls in all, what will be their respective numbers?

This kind of problem also occurs in the writings of Mahāvīra and of Bhāskara, but not in Brahmagupta. The version in *Bīja-Ganita* is :

Example of ancient authors : Five doves are to be had for three drammas ; seven cranes, for five ; nine geese, for seven ; and three peacocks, for nine : bring a hundred of these birds for a hundred drammas, for the prince's gratification.[1]

This characteristic development of the theory of indeterminate equations (in which there are more unknown quantities than there are equations with which to find them) occurs throughout the mediaeval period in both India and China. The only Greek works which *might* have had some initial influence are those of Diophantus *c.* A.D. 360 and Hypatia *c.* A.D. 400 which could have been carried to the East through Gundīshāpūr, but of these only some of the writings of Diophantus survive, and Hindu analysis proceeds much further. The words of H. T. Colebrooke are still significant :

Chiefly busied with indeterminate equations of the first degree, he

[1] Chapter VI, §§ 158–9.

(Diophantus) yet seems to have possessed no general rule for their solution. His elementary instructions for the preparation of equations are succinct. His notation, as before observed, scanty and inconvenient. In the whole science, he is very far behind the Hindu writers: notwithstanding the infinite ingenuity, by which he makes up for the want of rule: and although presented to us under the disadvantage of mutilation; if it be, indeed, certain that the text of only six, or at most seven, of thirteen books which his introduction announces has been preserved. It is sufficiently clear from what does remain, that the lost part could not have exhibited a much higher degree of attainment in the art. It is presumable, that so much as we possess of his work, is a fair specimen of the progress which he and the Greeks before him (for he is hardly to be considered as the inventor, since he seems to treat the art as already known;) had made in his time.

The points in which the Hindu Algebra appears particularly distinguished from the Greek, are, besides a better and more comprehensive algorithm,—1st, The management of equations involving more than one unknown term. (This adds to the two classes noticed by the Arabs, namely simple and compound, two, or rather three, other classes of equation). 2nd, The resolution of equations of a higher order, in which, if they achieved little, they had, at least, the merit of the attempt, and anticipated a modern discovery in the solution of biquadratics. 3rd, General methods for the solution of indeterminate problems of 1st and 2nd degrees, in which they went far, indeed, beyond Diophantus, and anticipated discoveries of modern Algebraists. 4th, Application of Algebra to astronomical investigation and geometrical demonstration: in which they also hit upon some matters which have been reinvented in later times.

Indeterminate equations of the first degree were described by the pulverizer (*kuṭṭaka*), i.e. to determine a "grinding or pulverizing multiplier"—a quantity such that, when it is multiplied by a given number, and the product added algebraically to a given quantity, the sum (or difference) is divisible by a given divisor without remainder. This may be expressed as

$$ax \pm \text{by} = c\,;$$

and the Hindu solution of x and y in whole numbers achieved essentially the same as did Euler's treatment in 1770 using continued fractions. This equation seems to have been first noted in Europe in 1624 by Bachet de Meziriac.

The Hindus excelled in their analysis of indeterminate equations of the second degree. Brahmagupta solved the equation $ax + by + c = xy$ in whole numbers, and also had some success with

$$ax^2 + c = y^2,$$

now called the Pellian equation. The full solution of the Pellian equation, and of its more general form $ax^2 + bx + c = y^2$, was given by Bhāskara, who developed the 'cyclic' method: of this method Hankel wrote: "It is beyond all praise: it is certainly the finest thing achieved in the theory of numbers before Lagrange."[1] We quote again from H. T. Colebrooke:

> Bháscara's second (cyclic) method (Víj. § 80–81) for the solution of the problem on which all indeterminate ones of this degree depend, is exactly the same, which Lord Brouncker devised to answer a question proposed by way of challenge by Fermat in 1657. The thing required was a general rule for finding the innumerable square numbers, which multiplied by a proposed (non-quadrate) number, and then assuming an unit, will make a square. Lord Brouncker's rule, putting n for any given number, r^2 for any square taken at pleasure, and d for difference between n and r^2 ($r^2 \sim n$) was $\dfrac{4r^2}{d^2} = \left(\dfrac{2r}{d} \times \dfrac{2r}{d}\right)$ the square required. In the Hindu rule, using the same symbols, $\dfrac{2r}{d}$ is the square root required. But neither Brouncker, nor Wallis, who himself contrived another

[1] H. Hankel, *Zur Geschichte der Mathematik*, p. 202. Leipzig, 1874.

method, nor Fermat, by whom the question was proposed, but whose mode of solution was never made known by him (probably because he had not found anything better than Wallis and Brouncker discovered), nor Frenicle, who treated the subject without, however, adding to what had been done by Wallis and Brouncker, appear to have been aware of the importance of the problem and its universal use: a discovery, which, among the moderns, was reserved for Euler in the middle of the last century. To him, among the moderns, we owe the remark, which the Hindus had made more than a thousand years before, that the problem was requisite to find all the possible solutions of equations of this sort. Lagrange takes credit for having further advanced the progress of this branch of the indeterminate analysis, so lately as 1767; and his complete solution of equations of the 2nd degree appeared no earlier than 1769.

(2)

Hindu mathematics presents interesting features of notation. Valuable information on this development is revealed by the Bakhshālī Manuscript. This manuscript, written in old Śāradā characters on seventy folios of birch-bark, was discovered in the extreme north-west of India in May 1881. Hoernle has dated the *mathematics* as early as the third or fourth century A.D., but Kaye classes it as a twelfth-century manuscript: Indian scholars again place some of its contents much earlier than does Hoernle. The manuscript was presented to the Bodleian Library, Oxford, by Dr. Hoernle in 1902.

In the Bakhshālī Manuscript we find a small sign used to represent negative quantity: it is a cross, like the present 'plus' sign, but placed to the right of the quantity to which it refers. Zero is represented by a dot. The dot is also used to indicate an unknown quantity. There is an absence from the Bakhshālī Manuscript of symbols of operation, even the negative sign already noted not being *used* as such. In Bhāskara's *Bīja-Ganita*, however, the dot is used as the *negative sign of operation* (see below). Operation is indicated in the Bakhshālī Manuscript by an *ad hoc* term, or by relative position, e.g.

Addition. 960 64 yutaṁ jātaṁ 1024
924 | 836 | 798 | eshāṁ yutiṁ kṛiyate jātā 2558

Subtraction. | 5 | 9 | viśeshaṁ | 4 |
| 5 | | 3 | rahitaṁ jātaṁ | 2 |

Multiplication. | 2 | dvigunaṁ | 4 |
| 30 | ashṭa gunaṁ | 240 |

Division.	168 4	168 6	168 7	labdhaṁ 42 | 28 | 24

Thus in division, or in writing fractions, the modern method is used but without the horizontal line. Abbreviations are numerous, e.g. bhā° for *bhāga*, divisor ; se° for *śeshaṁ*, remainder.

In general, Hindu mathematicians used the terms *yā* (from *yāvat tāvat*—" as many as ") for the first unknown quantity, now usually denoted by x ; *kā* (from *kālaka*—" black ") for the second unknown, say y ; *rū* (from *rūpa*) for the constant quantity in an expression ; *v* or *va* (from *varga*) for a square ; and the initial letters of the words representing various colours for other unknown quantities. Thus, in two simple instances :

yā 6 rū 300
yā 10 rū 10̇0

means in modern terms $6x + 300 = 10x - 100$.[1]

and

yā *v* 18 yā 0 rū 0
yā *v* 16 yā 9 rū 18

expresses $18x^2 - 0x + 0 = 16x^2 + 9x + 18$.[2]

[1] *Bīja-Ganita*, § 104. [2] *Bīja-Ganita*, § 132.

It has been generally believed that the so-called Arabic numerals, from which arise those in use by us today, were derived by the Muslim peoples from India, and that the Hindus invented (1) the principle of position or place value of the decimal point and (2) the nine digits and zero (or dot). Kaye held that no such system existed in India until the ninth century A.D., and both he and Carra de Vaux have argued in favour of the reverse process, namely, that the origin was Greek Neo-platonist and that the Hindus learned of them from the Muslim world. W. E. Clark has, however, put the evidence more fairly [1]; for instance, he says:

> Between A.D. 595 and the end of the ninth century about twenty inscriptions are known [in India] in which numerals with place value are used. The authenticity of some of these inscriptions has been questioned, but it is by no means certain that they are all to be brushed aside as forgeries. The matter will have to be decided by the judgment of expert epigraphists.

W. E. Clark also refuses to regard as worthless a statement made by F. Nau, which Kaye rejects, to the effect that the Indian numerals were known to a writer, Severus Sebokt, in a Syrian monastery on the upper Euphrates as early as A.D. 662 and had presumably come from India. The Babylonians, however, as we have already seen, had a rudimentary system involving place-value as early as 1700 B.C., and the whole history of numeration is in fact a very complex one: with regard to the immediate question of the transmission of the Hindu numerals in mediaeval times, we offer no final conclusion, as present evidence, both for and against Hindu origin, is capable of various interpretations: much critical work on Oriental manuscripts has yet to be carried out. Nevertheless, as was noted in

[1] *Legacy of India*, Clarendon Press, Oxford, p. 358.

Chapter III, scientific knowledge passed from India to China in the wake of Buddhism and there are plentiful references to Hindu mathematics and astronomy in the Catalogue, completed *c.* A.D. 610, of the Sui Dynasty ; indeed, in the astrological treatise written by Ch'ü-t'an Hsi-ta, who flourished under the T'ang Dynasty in the early eighth century A.D., the so-called Hindu decimal notation and rules are implied, so that they were introduced, or re-introduced into China, at that time or possibly earlier. Whereas Hindu astronomy made improvement through Greek influence, mathematics in India, as Professor Sarton has stated, had no need to wait for Hellenism : we are, therefore, at present disinclined to refuse legitimate claims for Hindu originality in respect of the nine numerals and decimal system.

(3)

The Hindu contribution to the origin of trigonometry requires a special note. The Greeks had worked in terms of chords and had used the ratio of the chord of the circle to its diameter. Ptolemy's chords were reckoned on a diameter of 120. By using the *half*-chord and a *radius* of 120 the Hindus obtained a table of sines directly and thus established the modern method of reckoning. The Sanskrit word *jyā* or *jīva* (from *ardhajyā* or *ardhajīva*, half-chord or bow-string) became in the Arabic firstly *jība* and then *jaib* (a curve or bay), and finally *sinus* in the mediaeval Latin, thus giving rise to the modern ' sine '.

The two main principles, by the aid of which the greater portion of all the Hindu calculations are made, are, on the one hand, the equality of the square of the hypotenuse in a right-angled triangle to the sum of the squares of the other two sides, and, on the other hand, the proportional relation of the corresponding parts of similar triangles. The first of these principles gave the Hindus the sine of the complement of any arc of which the sine was already known, it being equal to the square root of the difference between the squares of radius and of the given sine. This led further to the rule for finding the versed sine . . . : it was plainly equal to the difference between the sine complement and radius. Again, the comparison of similar triangles showed that the chord of an arc was a mean proportional between its versed sine and the diameter ; and this led to a method of finding the sine of half any arc of which the sine was known : it was equal to half the square root of the product of the diameter into the versed sine.[1]

Hindu shadow measurements on the gnomon also led to the adoption of the tangent and cotangent functions (from the *umbra versa* and *umbra extensa*), by Muslim scholars, especially the great astronomer Al-Battānī (known in mediaeval Europe as Albategnius), who lived *c.* A.D. 858–929.

The legacy of mediaeval Hindu science is not, however, by any means exhausted by the purely mathematical attainments, and we give two further instances of its richness and variety. The medical tradition of Suśruta was maintained, as indicated by the leaves of a birch-bark Sanskrit manuscript (the Bower Manuscript) found in Kuchā, Chinese Turkestan, in 1889, and dating from the fourth century A.D. Further, the metallurgical achievements displayed in the Iron Pillar of Delhi, pure, malleable, and rustless metal welded to a tapering cylinder, exceeding six tons in weight, and in the pure copper Buddha at Sultanganj made by casting, are achievements which inspire the highest respect ; both also date from *c.* A.D. 400.

[1] *Sūrya Siddhānta* (Burgess—Gangooly and Sengupta), Calcutta, 1935, p. 61.

4. *THE SCOPE OF ARABIC SCIENCE*

(i) THE ARABIC PERIOD AND THE DIFFUSION OF SCIENCE

A representative picture of Arabic science may be obtained by assessing it from the spatial, temporal, and intellectual aspects.

MUḤAMMAD died in A.D. 632. There followed a great wave of Muslim conquest which engulfed in rapid succession Syria and Mesopotamia (A.D. 638), Egypt (A.D. 640), and Persia (A.D. 641). By A.D. 665 there was regular settlement of the Arab invaders amongst the Berbers, and in A.D. 711 Arabs and Berbers entered Spain. This expansion came to an end in the south of France in the year A.D. 732, due to the opposition of Charles Martel, but Muslim influence lingered on in the University of Montpellier. The full extent of the Muslim world after stabilization may be appreciated from the words of the geographer Ibn Ḥauqal, writing *c.* A.D. 975:

> The length of the Empire of Islām in our days extends from the limits of Farghāna, passing through Khurāsān, Al-Jibāl, 'Irāq, and Arabia to the shores of Yamen, which is a journey of some four months; its breadth begins from the country of the Rūm, passing through Syria, Mesopotamia, 'Irāq, Fārs, and Kirmān, extending to the territory of al-Manṣūra on the coast of the Sea of Fārs, which represents about four months' journeying. . . .

But there is also

> the Maghrib and Andalus, because it resembles the sleeve of a garment. There is no Islām to the east and west of the Maghrib. If, however, one journeys beyond Egypt into the land of the Maghrib, there lie to

the south of it the lands of the Sūdān, and to its north the Sea of Rūm and then the territory of Rūm.[1]

From this vast area of Muslim influence, later extended to Samarkand, sprang institutions of learning from which emerged men of wide culture and of differing race whose works contributed to the glory of Arabic civilization. These centres were the means of intercourse between men and languages, a relationship no doubt furthered by the brotherhood of the pilgrimages to Mekka and Madinah, the caravan routes, and Arab maritime traffic. Science flourished equally in Córdoba and in Samarkand, though at different times.

Under the Emperor Justinian the schools of learning in Athens had been suppressed in the year 529. But for some five centuries before this event the Alexandrian School had retained the legacy of Greek science and mathematics, and Alexandria was still the focus of scientific learning in the world when the Muslim conquerors overran the city in 640 : though by that time Greek science had ceased to be a living force, stifled as such inquiry was by the prevailing faith in astrology and mysticism. Consequently, Greek thought did not pass to the Arabs through Alexandria so effectively as it did through the medium of the Syriac language ; the main transmission was effected through Syriac manuscripts by the Nestorian sect of Christians (founded in 428 by Nestorius, patriarch of Constantinople) who settled in Persia under the Sāsanian dynasty. A great Nestorian School was established at Jundīshāpūr in Khūzistān (S.W. Persia), and this became, as a result of the active participation of the king Chosroes Nūshīrwan in the sixth century A.D., the leading intellectual centre, where writings in Greek and Sanskrit were translated into Syriac and Pahlawi. When the Arabs overran Persia this

[1] *Legacy of Islam* (Arnold and Guillaume), Clarendon Press, Oxford, p. 80.

knowledge became available in Arabic. The Arab dynasty of the Umayyads, established in Damascus in 661, did not suppress existing cultural institutions, and until its overthrow in 749, Court physicians, often Jews and Christians of Arabic name, were drawn from Jundīshāpūr.

The Umayyads were succeeded by the Persian khalifs—the 'Abbāsids—and with these Arabic science entered its Golden Age. Representatives of the Umayyad family who could be located were slain by their successors, but one 'Abdu-r-Raḥman escaped to Spain, where his dynasty, which was founded at Córdoba in 755, ruled until 1030, and thus a glorious period of Muslim science came also to the Iberian peninsula. Al-Manṣūr became second 'Abbāsid khalif in 753 and some nine years later founded Baghdād. According to tradition, learned circles in that city knew in 773 of the *Sindhind*, probably the *Sūrya Siddhānta*, the astronomical treatise of the Hindus. The zenith of the Arabic science in the East was reached under its illustrious patron, the khalif Al-Ma'mūn, who reigned during the period 813–33 and established an academy (Bayt al-Ḥikma) and an observatory in Baghdād. The patronage of scholarship spread. Cairo, founded in 966, had also its "House of Wisdom" and library, due to the Fāṭimid astronomer-khalif al-Ḥākim.

After the energetic translation into Arabic in the ninth century, encouraged initially by Al-Ma'mūn, the works of Aristotle became generally known and appreciated. In the transmission of this Aristotelian and other Greek learning, there were many intermediaries—Nestorians, Jacobites, Zoroastrians, Pagans, and Jews—but after the assimilation of the older knowledge, science became essentially Muslim in character in the eleventh century, and the Muslim world began to add its own contribution. The Arab falasifa school, rationalist and objective, ultimately influenced the revival of Aristotelian learning in Latin Christendom.

It was in the romantic cities of Spain—Córdoba, Granada, Seville, Toledo—where Muslim, Christian, and Jewish influences commingled, that the legacy of the Greek genius, preserved and supplemented by the Arabic, came to enter largely into western Europe. Córdoba, in the tenth century, was a great centre of learning, where one could walk for several miles in a straight line by the light of the public lamps: under the Umayyad khalif Al-Ḥakam (A.D. 961–76) it emulated the glorious achievement of the 'Abbāsid khalif Al-Ma'mūn at Baghdād of some one hundred and fifty years earlier. Instrumental in the propagation of learning were Raymond, Archbishop of Toledo, in the twelfth century, and Alfonso X of León and Castile, in the late thirteenth century. This transmission to Europe was further aided by the enthusiasm of the Emperor Frederick II of Sicily, who founded the University of Naples in 1224. Here Arabic manuscripts were eagerly translated into Latin or Hebrew. Latin translations were also presented by Frederick II to the University of Bologna. The direction of thought in the mediaeval universities of Europe was strongly influenced by the writings of Ibn Sīnā (Avicenna), A.D. 980–1037, the last of the great Eastern Arabic philosophers, and Ibn Rushd (Averroës), A.D. 1126–98, the greatest philosopher of Muslim Spain.

In respect of Muslim contacts further east, we have the testimony of Al-Bīrūnī in his famous work on India. Al-Bīrūnī (A.D. 973–1048) was a contemporary of the poet Firdausī in the reign of Maḥmūd of Ghazna, and one of the greatest geniuses of all time. Muslim influences penetrated to Central Asia and reached their zenith in science in the reign of Ulūgh Beg, a prince of the house of Tamerlane, who erected at Samarkand the finest astronomical observatory of his time and arranged the astronomical tables which bear his name. These tables, which appeared in 1437, were still influential two hundred years later, and were translated from the Persian and used by John Greaves, Savilian Professor of Astronomy at Oxford in the reign of Charles I. It is interesting to note that the Giralda Tower, close by Seville Cathedral, formed the first astronomical observatory in Europe, and that Muslim astronomical technique as carried on in far-away Samarkand still led the world as late as 1437.

The last word has not been said concerning the complex problem of the transmission of scientific knowledge to and from the Arabs. Exaggerated statements have sometimes been made on insufficient evidence. The position may be judged with the help of two quotations from Professor Sarton.[1]

Fritz Saxl had stated (1912) that the Islamitic representations of planets of the XIIth century and later times were directly based on Babylonian traditions, the chief transmitters being the Haranite Sabeans. Yet this theory is quite insufficient to bridge the huge cleft between ancient Babylon and the XIIth century. Ruska maintains that these planetary representations, like astrology itself, are rooted in the Orientalized Hellenistic world. It was difficult to prove it however on the basis of the astrological literature, but Ruska has now established this filiation on the basis of Arabic lapidaries of the Bibliothèque Nationale [in Paris], dealing chiefly with the engraving of planetary representations on their symbolic stones.

. . . .

Ruska's main conclusions [on early Arabic mathematics] have the more weight in that they are more cautious. Indian influences on Arabic mathematics seem to him to have been far greater than is generally admitted ; Greek influences on the contrary, smaller, although he is less positive on this second point. We must remember that the Greek sources became generally accessible by translations only in the IXth and Xth centuries. This conclusion is entirely at variance with Kaye's conclusion, but the latter has made no first hand study of the Arabic texts. Hence we must give more weight to Ruska's judgment :—

[1] *Isis*, III, pp. 476–7, 1921.

Ruska's investigation is the more important in that Rosen's translation of Al-Khowarizmi's Algebra (1831) is not always correct.

We now proceed to amplify this brief survey by studying in some detail the achievements of the more eminent Arabic scientists.

(ii) SOME GREAT ARABIC THINKERS AND EXPERIMENTERS

The second half of the eighth century A.D. was a period of transmission of knowledge to the Arabs, and scholars were mainly concerned in translation and elaboration of texts from the Syriac, Pahlawi, Greek, and Sanskrit, particularly under the second and fifth 'Abbāsid khalifs Al-Manṣūr (754–75) and Hārūn al-Rashīd (786–809). Under the former the city of Baghdad was planned by the Jewish astronomer and astrologer Māshallāh and the Persian astronomer and engineer Al-Naubakht, and the translation of the Hindu astronomy defined by the term *siddhānta* was made by Muḥammad ibn Ibrāhīm al-Fazārī.

The first great name is that of Jābir ibn Ḥayyan, the alchemist who flourished *c.* 776 in Kūfa. Jābir was the author of many chemical treatises, and the Jābirian corpus of writings (by himself or his followers) is so vast, and as yet not completely evaluated, that we are unable to judge clearly such a great personality. Mediaeval Latin versions of his works appeared under the name Geber.

Jābir's practical knowledge of chemical processes was extensive : for instance, he knew how to produce concentrated acetic acid by the distillation of vinegar, the use of manganese dioxide in glass-manufacture, and the preparation of arsenic and antimony from their sulphides ; and he studied the refinement of metals, the manufacture of steel, and processes of dyeing. On the theoretical side he upheld a theory of metals which attributed their different properties to the relative proportion in them of two fundamental substances mercury and sulphur; he also studied the geological formation of metals. His alchemical writings include *The Book of Mercy*, *The Book of Concentration*, *The Little Book of the Balances*, *The Book of the Kingdom*, and *The Book of Eastern Mercury*. Though loaded with alchemical doctrine, Jābir's writings contain much sound chemical technique.

In the ninth century the work of translation and assimilation went on. The seventh 'Abbāsid khalif, Al-Ma'mūn (813–33), a great patron of science, sent a mission to the Byzantine emperor, Leon the Armenian, to collect Greek manuscripts, and established The Abode of Wisdom (Bayt al-ḥikma) at Baghdad, which was the most effective academy of science since the Museum of Alexandria. During his khalifate and later, there flourished Al-Kindī. Al-Kindī, like many eminent scholars of the Middle Ages, was an encyclopaedist, and wrote numerous works on many subjects. He translated extensively from the Greek, and his treatise on geometrical and physiological optics (known in the Latin form as *De Aspectibus*) was based on the optical works of Euclid, Heron, and Ptolemy. He was interested in large-scale natural phenomena, studying particularly the tides, and also the rainbow in accordance with the principles of optical reflection. Further, his scientific studies embraced the Hindu numerals and a musical notation relating to pitch. He was sufficiently far-sighted to regard much alchemy as spurious and non-scientific. Al-Kindī died *c.* 875.

Eminent among writers on mechanical and mathematical subjects were the three sons of Mūsā ibn Shākir, the Banū Mūsā, who engaged also the great translators Ḥunain ibn Isḥāq and Thābit ibn Qurra. Among the various writings attributed to the Banū Mūsā is the *Book of the Balance*, a treatise dealing with weighing. They also knew the construction of an ellipse by means of a string connecting the foci.

There also flourished under Al-Ma'mūn the great mathematician Muḥammad ibn Mūsā al-Khuwārizmī, who was born at Khuwārizm (Khiva) and who was the most influential of mediaeval mathematicians. He fused Hindu and Greek mathematical knowledge, and from his work derive the terms algorism and algebra. His arithmetic introduced the Hindu numeral system to the Arabs and the West; his Algebra gave solutions of linear and quadratic equations, and also a neat geometrical illustration of the solution of the quadratic,

$$x^2 + 10x = 39,$$

by 'the completion of the square'. As this particular illustration was repeated in later Arabic works, even in the Algebra of 'Umar Khayyām, it is set forth here:

Let us imagine that x^2 is the square whose side x is to be found. If we suppose the square to be drawn and then increased by the addition of four rectangles, each of area $2\frac{1}{2}$ times x, along its four sides, then the whole area is $x^2 + 10x$. To make a new and larger square we must 'complete' this square by the addition of the four small squares, at each of the four corners of the original x^2. Each small square has an area of $(2\frac{1}{2} \times 2\frac{1}{2})$ i.e. $6\frac{1}{4}$, and their total area is 25. Our final square is

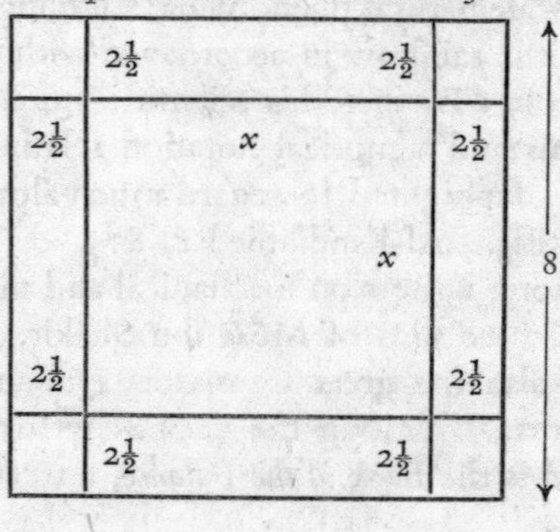

thus of area $x^2 + 10x + 25$. But $x^2 + 10x = 39$, hence $x^2 + 10x + 25$ must equal $39 + 25$, or 64. So 64 is also the area of the final square. The side of this final square is clearly 8. By subtracting from both ends of the side (8) of this square the two lengths of $2\frac{1}{2}$, we obtain the required value of x, which is seen to be 3.

Mathematicians will know of a further solution, which is $x = -13$, but the Arabic scholars dealt only with the positive answer. Unlike the Chinese and Hindus, they tended to ignore negative quantities. Mathematical tables, compiled by Al-Khuwārizmī and revised by Al-Majrīṭī, contained values of the sine and tangent of angles, and were introduced to Europe in the Latin translation of Adelard of Bath in 1126. Al-Khuwārizmī also improved the Geography of Ptolemy.

Another great name associated with the reign of Al-Ma'mūn is that of Al-Farghānī. It will have been seen already from what distant and diverse places in the Islamic world these learned men came, and Al-Farghānī was born at Farghānā in Transoxiana. The twelfth-century Latin version of his *Elements of Astronomy* influenced European workers in that science till the time of Regiomontanus.

Al-Battānī, one of the most eminent of Islamic astronomers, was born, probably before 853, in or near Ḥarran, and died in 929 near Sāmarrā: he was of Ṣābian origin though a Muslim. He made remarkably accurate astronomical observations and compiled a catalogue of fixed stars. His great treatise, known in the mediaeval Latin as *De scientia stellarum*, which influenced European astronomy until the Renaissance, contains valuable material in trigonometry, including the use of the cotangent and of the formula relating the sides and angles of a spherical triangle.

At about the same time there also flourished Al-Rāzī (Rhazes), who was not only an outstanding physician but also possessed a competent knowledge of physical and chemical subjects which he applied to medicine. His extensive writings include the *Kitāb al-ḥāwī* (Latin *Continens*), a monumental medical encyclopaedia, and also an important specialist work on measles and smallpox. Professor Sarton's words are to the point: "The greatest clinician of Islam and of the Middle Ages. Galenic in theory, he combined with his immense learning true Hippocratic wisdom." [1]

We have already mentioned Ḥunain ibn Isḥāq, but his great zeal and industry in preparing authoritative translations demand some further recognition. He was a Nestorian physician and worked firstly at Jundīshāpūr, and then at Baghdad, thus representing in himself one of the most significant cultural movements in history. Professor Sarton's words are again pertinent:

> His methods remind one of modern methods. . . . His activity was prodigious; it began as early as *c.* 826 and lasted until the end of his days. It is typical of his scientific honesty that he very severely criticized the translations made by himself early in life. As his experience increased, his scientific ideal became more exacting. He translated a great many of Galen's works, also various writings of Hippocrates, Plato, Aristotle, and Dioscorides, and Ptolemy's *Quadripartitum*. The importance of this activity can be measured in another way by stating that the translations prepared by Ḥunain and his school were the foundation of that Muslim canon of knowledge which dominated medical thought almost to modern times. [2]

We mention, in passing, two men, namely, Al-Fārābī and Al Mas'ūdī, who were famous in very different spheres of activity but whose great knowledge embraced practically the whole science of their day. Al-Fārābī, "The Second Teacher" after Aristotle, famous as a philosopher, wrote treatises on the fundamental principles of science and a valuable work on the theory

[1] Sarton, *Introduction to the History of Science*, I, 609.

[2] *Ibid.*, p. 611.

of music. He studied in Aleppo and in Damascus, where he died *c.* 950. Al-Mas'ūdī, the traveller and geographer, sometimes compared to Pliny, wrote the encyclopaedia entitled *Meadows of Gold and Mines of Precious Stones*, in which there is the first mention of the existence of windmills (in Sijistān, i.e. Afghānistān), and *The Book of Indication and Revision*, which mentions an evolutionary process through the mineral, plant, and animal stages, successively, to man.

Towards the end of the tenth century A.D. the enlightened patronage of science and letters which had characterized the 'Abbāsid khalifs in Baghdad began to manifest itself through the Umayyad dynasty in Spain. Córdova became " The Jewel of the World ", the intellectual focus of Europe. Al-Ḥakam II, the ninth Umayyad khalif in Spain, kept abreast of events in the East and amassed a great library of some 400,000 volumes. As a result of this respect for scholarship, Al-Andalus and Al-Maghrib, i.e. Western Islām, began to produce also its own great thinkers, and we shall encounter some of their names presently. Often these were Spanish-Jewish philosophers such as Ibn Gabirol ; and later on such men played a prominent part in the transmission of Arabic knowledge into Latin.

Also at Baṣra there was formed *c.* 983 a secret brotherhood known as the Ikhwān al-ṣafā' (Brethren of Sincerity), whose encyclopaedia of knowledge, comprising fifty-two treatises, had considerable influence. The Brethren of Sincerity tried to reconcile Greek scientific thought with the Qur'ān. They were particularly interested in large-scale natural events, such as earthquakes, the tides, and eclipses, and they considered that sound consists of a vibration of the air.

Astronomy and mathematics continued to flourish throughout the Muslim world. Abū'l Wafā' (940–98), who worked in Baghdad, made a special study of practical problems in geometry which can be solved by one opening of the compass, obtained geometrical solutions of certain equations of the fourth degree, and made new advances in the study of trigonometrical tables and formulae ; Ibn Yūnus completed in 1007 in Cairo, under the patronage of the Fāṭimid khalif Al-Ḥākim, the improved astronomical tables known as the *Hakemite Tables*, facilitated methods of calculation by the use of the formulae of plane trigonometry, and solved problems of spherical trigonometry by orthogonal projection ; improved methods in arithmetic also resulted from the work of Al-Karkhī and al-Nasawī, the latter using decimal fractions.

In the West, during the khalifate of Al-Ḥakam II (961–76), medicine flourished at Córdova through the Court physicians, the Spanish-Jewish Ḥasdai ibn Shaprut, and one of great fame in Latin Christendom, Albucasis or Abū'l-Qāsim. The latter was an eminent surgeon whose treatise on surgery, illustrated with diagrams of the instruments, formed part of his large medical encyclopaedia. Spain also produced makers of beautiful and accurate observational instruments ; in particular, in the eleventh century, Al-Zarqālī invented the *ṣafīḥa*, an improved form of the astrolabe. Al-Zarqālī also edited the *Toledan Tables*, giving planetary positions based on observations made at Toledo.

The East at this time produced three of its greatest sons, Al-Bīrūnī, Ibn Sīnā (Avicenna), and Ibn Al-Haitham. The Persian Al-Bīrūnī (973–1048)—" The Master "—was a contemporary of the epic-poet Firdausī in the reign of Maḥmūd of Ghazna in Afghānistān. He ranks as one of the greatest scientists of all time. In the course of his travels in India he made a deep study of Sanskrit literature and was influential in the transmission of scientific ideas between India and Islām. Amongst his major writings are an encyclopaedia of astronomy, his *Chronology of Ancient Nations* (dealing in part with the calendars), and the *Ta'rīkh al-Hind*, an account of the religion, philosophy, literature, geography, chronology, astronomy, customs, laws, and astrology of India about A.D. 1030. Al-Bīrūnī also determined accurately the relative densities of metals and precious stones, explained natural springs and 'artesian' wells by the principles of hydrostatics, and the Indus Valley as an ancient sea-bed filled by alluvions. He gave the best mediaeval account of the Hindu numerals and the principle of position, and investigated certain mathematical problems which are insoluble by the use of ruler and compasses alone—e.g. the trisection of an angle—and which involve the intersection of conics. This investigation of problems by the intersection of conics, including as it does the solution of cubic equations, was a special feature of mediaeval Arabic mathematics, and several leading mathematicians such as Al-Māhānī, Al-Khāzin, Al-Kūhī, Al-Sijzī, Abū'l Jūd, and 'Umar Khayyām made their contributions to it.

Ibn Sīnā, the most famous of Islamic scientists, was born near Bukhārā in Central Asia in 980 and died at Hamadhān in 1037. According to Professor Sarton, " His triumph was too complete; it discouraged original investigations and sterilized intellectual life. Like Aristotle and Vergil, Avicenna was considered by the people of later times as a magician " . . . " one may say that his thought represents the climax of mediaeval philosophy ".[1] He is noted particularly (1) for his great *Qānūn* (Canon) of medicine, of a million words, which, though an encyclopaedic compilation, contains some good observations, such as a clear description of skin diseases, and (2) for his encyclopaedia of philosophy (*Kitāb al-shifā'*), which includes his views on the principles of physical science and on musical intervals, the treatment of the latter being superior to the *Kitāb al-mūsīqī* of Al-Fārābī. The *Qānūn* had an important influence upon the

[1] Sarton, *op. cit.*, I, p. 711.

European medical schools which lasted for six hundred years, and it is still authoritative in Islām to-day. The mediaeval Latin translation was made by Gerard of Cremona in the twelfth century and various printed editions appeared in the Italian medical centres before 1500, e.g. in Padua, 1476. On physical and chemical questions Ibn Sīnā held views which were in advance of his times: for instance, he regarded light as an emission by the luminous source of particles travelling at a finite speed, and placed no reliance upon attempts at transmutation of the metals which took account of colouring, for he realized that chemical processes are more fundamental than such superficial qualities would indicate. Ibn Sīnā also studied the nature of heat, and of force and motion, and certain aspects of geology.

Ibn Al-Haitham (Alhazen) was born at Baṣra *c.* 965 and died in Cairo in 1039. He was the *true* physicist of mediaeval Islām, just as Archimedes had been in his own Greek times, for he combined with rare skill both the experimental investigation of natural phenomena and the analysis of results by mathematics. Others, such as Ibn Sīnā, were occupied with wider philosophical implications, and were indeed limited as experimenters by their synthetic tendencies. In fact, mediaeval science tried to make a complete world picture, subordinated to theology and into which explanations of phenomena were neatly fitted. Ibn Al-Haitham resembles more the scientists of the European Renaissance of the seventeenth century, and one is not surprised therefore to learn that his influence continued through Robert Grosseteste—Bishop of Lincoln, and another Franciscan—his pupil Roger Bacon, also John Peckham, Witelo, Leonardo da Vinci, and Johannes Kepler. The printed Latin edition of his *Optics* first appeared in Basle in 1572.

The researches of Ibn Al-Haitham were mainly in optics. He investigated plane and parabolic mirrors, making his own mirrors out of steel on a kind of lathe, and from the mathematics of ray diagrams discussing the phenomenon of spherical aberration ; he made the first elaborate studies of refraction, though he failed to discover the Law later obtained by Snell in 1621, and in this field (which had been scarcely opened by the Greeks) he dealt also with the magnification of a lens and with atmospheric refraction ; his knowledge of the mechanism of the eye was considerable, and with Ibn Sīnā and Al-Bīrūnī he thought that rays of light passed from the luminous object to the eye, a view contrary to that of Euclid and Ptolemy, who had believed that the rays originated from the eye itself ; further, he carried out a detailed study of rays of light passing through a small aperture and so made use of the camera obscura ; and finally, he obtained a solution, by means of the intersection of a circle and a hyperbola, of a problem involving an equation of the fourth degree, and which may be stated in modern terms thus :

Given the position of an object *O* and of the observer *I* in front of a concave spherical mirror *M* to determine the point of reflection *M* of the ray *OMI*. (Alhazen's Problem.)

Ibn Al-Haitham just failed to enunciate several important generalizations in physics, though they are often implicit in his thought. For instance, he stated that a ray of light, in passing through a medium, takes the path which is the 'easier and quicker', thereby anticipating Fermat's discovery of the Principle of Least Time ; he also understood the Principle of Inertia, later stated explicitly as Newton's First Law of Motion, in the science of mechanics ; and he discussed the process of refraction in mechanical terms by considering the movement of the 'particle' of light, as it passed through the surface of separation of two media, in accordance with the rectangle of forces, a mode of approach later elaborated by Sir Isaac Newton. It is a pity that

Al-Haitham's careful investigation into refraction did not lead him to the fact that, for a ray of light passing from one medium to another, the ratio of the sine of the angle of incidence (measured from the normal of the surface of separation of the media) to the sine of the angle of refraction is a definite number for the two given media (Snell's Law), because reckoning by the sines of angles had become well known to Muslim scientists by that time.

The publication of Edward Fitzgerald's translation of the *Rubā'īyāt* in 1859 led in due course to a wide appreciation in the Western world of the Persian poetry of 'Umar Khayyām. As a result of this, the scientific writings of 'Umar Khayyām, which were in Arabic and were a product of the *major* occupation of his life, have suffered from neglect. In fact, 'Umar Khayyām was astronomer to the Saljūq sultān, Jalāl al-Dīn, for whom *c.* 1075 he reformed the calendar and made it probably superior to the Gregorian; he investigated methods of determining relative densities of materials; and he wrote a treatise on Algebra, which was the most advanced work of its kind, and places him amongst the greatest of mathematicians of the East. The *Algebra* of 'Umar Khayyām gave an elaborate classification of equations, treated of equations of the second degree both geometrically and algebraically, and dealt with the solution of cubic equations in terms of solid geometry and by the intersection of conic sections. The last development was the climax of a line of thought which occupied his predecessors, beginning, as we have previously noted, with Al-Māhānī, and which derives initially from Archimedes. 'Umar Khayyām evolved a geometrical algebra, which, in a sense, anticipated the algebraical geometry developed by Descartes over five hundred years later (1637). Though we must be careful not to confuse these two aspects of the study of the conic sections, we cannot fail to note the originality of 'Umar Khayyām, who died at or near Nīshāpūr as early as *c.* 1123, and whose *Algebra* came to Europe, not in mediaeval Latin translation, but only in four Arabic manuscripts [1] found in the libraries of India—and now in Paris, Leyden, and London—long after the reputation of Descartes had been firmly established. It is interesting to speculate upon the effect such a Latin version of this *Algebra* might have had upon the course of the Renaissance in European Science—and indeed also of all the books mentioned in the *Fihrist al-'ulūm* (*Index of the Sciences*) completed by al-Nadīm *c.* 988 and of which *almost all* were destroyed in the sacking of Baghdad by the Mongols in 1258. Such catastrophes in the history of civilization engender sober thought on the frailty of human nature and on the imperative duty to maintain and preserve the sum of human knowledge.

By the middle of the twelfth century Arabic science was generally in decline. There were, however, developments in mechanics, which though not very original in theory, displayed remarkable ingenuity in construction and beauty of design. Most of this work was based upon the *Mechanics* of Hero of Alexandria and the *Pneumatics* of Philo of Byzantium and the applications initiated in the ninth century by the Banū Mūsā. Interest was centred around the determination of relative densities by the Principle of Archimedes, the lever and the balance, and the use of hydraulic contrivances such as water-clocks, water-wheels, and fountains. Al-Khāzinī of Merv completed *c.* 1122 a remarkable treatise entitled *The Book of the Balance of Wisdom*, which gives a good account of the mechanics and hydrostatics of his day, and also contains the theory of a universal force of gravity directed towards the centre of the earth, the assumption that air has weight, and some observations

[1] A fifth, now in America, was purchased in 1931 by Professor David Eugene Smith from a Persian dealer in Lahore.

on capillarity. Al-Khāzinī also completed the *Sinjaric astronomical tables*. At the beginning of the thirteenth century two technological books were completed, one about the famous clock installed in the Bāb Jairūn at Damascus, and written *c.* 1203 by Ibn al-Sā'ātī, and the other a valuable work by Al-Jazarī, written *c.* 1205, which dealt mainly with hydraulic apparatus.

A fine medical tradition, however, was being maintained in Spain by the Ibn Zuhr family, of which the most famous member was Abū Marwān Ibn Zuhr (Avenzoar). Ibn Zuhr flourished in Seville, where he was born soon after 1090, and he died in that city *c.* 1162. He *specialized* as a physician, and has left three important works : (1) The *Kitāb al-iqtiṣād* which deals with psychology, therapeutics, and hygiene ; (2) the *Kitāb al-taisīr*, written at the request of Ibn Rushd, and treating of pathological conditions, therapeutics, diet, and prescriptions ; and (3) the *Kitāb al-aghdhiya*, dealing mainly with foodstuffs and drugs. The *Kitāb al-taisīr* contains some excellent clinical observations relating to such disorders as inflammation of the middle ear, pharyngeal paralysis, and mediastinal tumours ; it was translated into Hebrew before 1260 and into Latin *c.* 1280, and maintained its influence upon European medicine until the end of the seventeenth century. Western Islām also produced another leading physician, who, however, achieved great renown as a philosopher, namely Ibn Rushd (Averroës). Ibn Rushd was born at Córdova in 1126, and was for some twelve years physician to the Almohade khalifs at Marrākush, where he died in 1198. His writings were very extensive, and included many commentaries, especially upon the biological and physical works of Aristotle, but also one upon Galen's *Treatise on Fevers*. The complex history of Averroism is beyond the scope of this little book, and reference will be made only to the *Kullīyāt*. The

Kitāb al-kullīyāt fī-l-ṭibb was a medical encyclopaedia dealing with anatomy and physiology; pathology and diagnosis; hygiene, therapeutics, and materia medica; and was smaller and less valuable than Ibn Sīnā's *Qānūn*. It was translated into Latin at Padua by a Jewish scholar Bonacosa in 1255. Ibn Rushd understood the functioning of the retina of the eye. Finally, this brief mention of medicine in Western Islam would be incomplete without the name of the Jewish thinker Maimonides and of the illustrious medical family to which he belonged. As with Averroës, his name to most people stands for his philosophy, but its profound influence cannot be discussed here. Maimonides (Moses ben Maimon) was born in Córdova in 1135, and died in Cairo in 1204; his tomb is to be seen at Tiberias in Palestine. Whilst in Cairo he was physician to Ṣalāḥ al-Dīn (Saladin), and his medical writings, quite apart from the philosophical ones, had great effect in mediaeval Europe. Amongst these may be quoted (1) the *Medical Principles or Fuṣūl Mūsā* (*Moses' Aphorisms*), based mainly on Galen though with criticisms of his work, and containing chapters on anatomy, physiology, pathology; symptoms and diagnosis; aetiology; therapeutics; fevers; cathartics, emetics, and blood-letting; surgery; gynaecology; hygiene, massage, and gymnastics; dietetics and drugs; (2) the *Maqāla fī-tadbīr al-ṣiḥḥa*, giving a regimen relating to diet, hygiene, and psychotherapy for the eldest son of Ṣalāḥ al-Dīn, who suffered from melancholia; (3) the *Kitāb al-sumūm*, which deals with poisons and antidotes; and (4) treatises on asthma and on haemorrhoids. The work of Maimonides, though it made use of that of Al-Rāzī, Ibn Sīnā, Ibn Wāfid, and Ibn Zuhr, contains some valuable instances of direct observation, e.g. a clinical description of belladonna poisoning; the testing of pulse and of urine in diagnosis.

Meanwhile Islām was producing its greatest botanist and

pharmacist, Ibn Al-Baiṭār. Ibn Al-Baiṭār was a Spanish Muslim who travelled extensively in North Africa and the Middle East in search of plants and who died in Damascus in 1248, two years before the burial of Frederick II in Palermo. He is noted for two works, the *Kitāb al-jāmiʿ fī-l-adwiya al-mufrada*, dealing with plants, drugs, and foods, and the *Kitāb al-mughnī fī-l-adwiya al-mufrada*, which treats of the same subject from the aspect of therapeutics; thus, whilst the former work is primarily a natural history, the latter is one of materia medica.

Even in the general decline of Arabic science the mathematical and astronomical labours continued in both Eastern and Western Islām, and remained conspicuous to the fifteenth century. There were such men as Al-Ḥasan Al-Marrākushī, who wrote the *Jamiʿ al-mabādī wa-l-ghāyāt* (probably *c.* 1230), which elaborated the graphical methods and the trigonometry, required in the solution of astronomical problems, arising out of the refinement of the instruments of measurement such as the gnomon, quadrant, astrolabe, and planisphere; Abū-l-Faraj (Barhebraeus), 1226–1286, the Syriac encyclopaedist, who wrote a summary of Ptolemy's *Almagest*; Ibn Al-Bannāʿ, the Moroccan mathematician and astronomer, who wrote at least fifty works, including a very popular treatise on the methods of calculation, entitled *Talkhīṣ fī aʿmāl al-ḥisāb*, and containing the use of the Hindu numerals in their Western (ghubār) form, a better treatment of fractions, and the summation of the squares and cubes of the natural numbers; Al-ʿUrḍī and Muḥyī al-Dīn Al-Maghribī, who both worked in the Mongol observatory of Hūlāgū Khān established at Marāgha *c.* 1259, and Nāṣir al-Dīn Al-Ṭūsī (1201–74), the famous director of that observatory; and finally, Quṭb al-Dīn Al-Shīrāzī (1236–1311) and Kamāl al-Dīn Al-Fārisī (died *c.* 1320), two of the greatest of Persian scientists, who excelled in the study of optics.

The observatory and library at Marāgha in Adharbāijān was established soon after the overthrow of the 'Abbāsid khalifate and the sacking of Baghdad by Hūlāgū Khān, who employed Nāṣir al-Dīn al-Ṭūsī as his astrologer. Al-Ṭūsī was also the first director of the observatory and was succeeded by two of his sons. The instruments made in the foundry and toolshop under Al-'Urḍī's supervision became renowned for their accuracy and workmanship, and the extensive library contained many volumes acquired during the Mongol campaigns ; but this rich establishment seems, like other such institutions, to have depended very much upon the interest of the ruling sovereign, as did the later observatory at Samarkand, and both had a brief life, that at Marāgha of perhaps two generations, that at Samarkand even less. Several competent assistants were collected at Marāgha by Al-Ṭūsī from different parts of the Muslim world, and it is probable that Chinese astronomers went there at the invitation of Hūlāgū : indeed, during the period of Mongol supremacy in Central Asia during the thirteenth and fourteenth centuries culture and trade alike passed freely along the great caravan routes linking China with the West.

Whilst Hūlāgū was Īlkhān of Persia (1256–65), Al-Ṭūsī was instructed to compile a new set of astronomical tables : these *Ilkhānian Tables* dealing with Greek, Chinese, Persian, and Arabic chronology, planetary motions, ephemerides and astrology, occupied the observatory staff some twelve years, *c.* 1260–72, and comprised both new observations and the earlier results of Hipparchos, Ptolemy, and the Muslim astronomers such as Ibn Yūnus, being widely known even in China and later influencing John Greaves (1602–52) at Oxford. The instruments used in making the observations included amongst others the mural quadrant, the armillary sphere, solstitial and equinoctial armils, and the alidade : and there were trigonometrical instruments used to determine sines and versed sines of angles.

Al-Ṭūsī wrote extensively in a variety of subjects ranging over music and poetry, logic and ethics, theology and philosophy, and several sciences. He edited a great collection of Arabic writings which were mainly based upon the Greek authors, e.g. Aristarchos, Euclid, Apollonios, Archimedes, Ptolemy; and to which were added later certain works by Thābit ibn Qurra, by the Banū Mūsā, and by himself; this collection was known as the *Mutawassiṭāt*, and according to Professor Sarton—"Together with the *Elements* and the *Almagest*, the *Mutawassiṭāt* constituted the bulk of ancient classics available to the Muslims."[1] Al-Ṭūsī is also famous for his *Shakl al-qaṭṭa'*, the first treatise dealing exclusively with trigonometry, and which ranks with the work of Regiomontanus printed in 1533; it contains an elaborate treatment of the solution of plane and spherical triangles; and the method of polar triangles, later dealt with by Vieta (1593) and Snell (1627), is implied in his working. The most important of the astronomical treatises of Al-Ṭūsī was the *Tadhkira*, which gave rise to a series of commentaries in the East reaching to the sixteenth century; it failed to improve upon the *Almagest*, but the criticisms of Ptolemy's conclusions which it made were a valuable new departure from accepted mediaeval practice.

The most famous pupil of Al-Ṭūṣī was Quṭb al-Dīn al-Shīrāzī, who wrote mainly about astronomical and medical subjects. His *Nihāyat*, though based largely upon the *Tadhkira* of his master, exhibits a wide range of material, including besides astronomical questions, much meteorology, mechanics, optics, and geodesy; he gives the first explanation of the rainbow (though not of its separate colours) in terms of reflection *and*

[1] Sarton, *op. cit.*, II, p. 1002.

refraction of light rays in the water-drops, thus anticipating Descartes. The Muslim tradition in optics was continued through Quṭb al-Dīn to his own pupil Kamāl al-Dīn al-Fārisī. The *Optics* (*Kitāb al-Manāẓir*) of Ibn al-Haitham became known to Kamāl al-Dīn when Quṭb al-Dīn made a reference to it. As a result, Kamāl al-Dīn prepared a full commentary upon it and several small writings of Al-Haitham under the title *Tanqīḥ al-Manāẓir*. Nevertheless, the *Tanqīḥ* exhibited considerable originality and anticipated Leonardo da Vinci in some respects; amongst Kamāl al-Dīn's ideas will be found a good account of the refraction of light, including the assumption that the speed of light is in inverse ratio to the optical (not material) density of the medium in which it is travelling; the suggestion that hyperboloidal lenses might avoid spherical aberration, a defect which Al-Haitham had noted with concave surfaces; an improved knowledge of the camera obscura; and finally, as with Al-Haitham, an understanding of the resolution and compounding of forces.

The study of the eye was an important subject in Arabic science, owing to the prevalence of eye diseases, and the optical knowledge was reinforced by considerable medical skill. Among those physicians who wrote on ophthalmology in the thirteenth century were Ibn Al-Nafīs, Ṣalāḥ al-Dīn Ibn Yūsuf, and Khalīfa ibn Abī-l-Maḥāsin, all of whom flourished in Syria. The *Kitāb al-kāfī fī-l-kuḥl* (c. 1265) of Khalīfa ibn Abī-l-Maḥāsin is particularly noteworthy as a systematic treatise for the oculist, and deals with the anatomy of the eye, its fluids, vision, nerves, and muscles, and with symptoms of diseases and their treatment by drugs; there is a schematic diagram of the eye and brain, and illustrations of the instruments of the oculist are shown. In the words of Professor Sarton—"Khalīfa was obviously a practitioner of great experience, who was so sure of himself that he did not fear to operate the cateract of a one-eyed man. Some operations are minutely described by him."[1] Ibn Al-Nafīs was especially noted for his commentaries upon the *Qānūn* of Ibn Sīnā, namely, *Al-Mūjiz* and *Sharḥ tashrīḥ*. The latter work is partly physiological and suggests that the venous blood cannot pass from the right to the left ventricle of the heart through pores in the septum, but that there must be a circulation by artery to the lungs, to make contact with the air, and a return to the left ventricle by vein. Should this statement be confirmed by further research on the manuscripts it would make Ibn Al-Nafīs, as Professor Sarton indicates, a notable precursor of William Harvey (*De motu cordis*, 1628). The Arabic tradition in ophthalmology which goes back to the beginning of the ninth century can be said to end with a valuable treatise, *Kitāb al-'umda*, written probably in the second half of the fourteenth century by the Egyptian Al-Shādhilī, and containing a description of the development of trachoma and information about other affections of the eyelids, such as lid cancer. The standard of medical practice generally was maintained in Islām by such men as Ḥājjī Pāshā, a Turk who became chief physician at the Bīmāristān al-Manṣūrī, the great hospital founded in Cairo in 1284, and who gave a valuable description of the symptoms of pneumonia ; Manṣūr ibn Muḥammad, the Persian physician and anatomist who completed *c.* 1396 a treatise on anatomy illustrated by five coloured diagrams ; and Ibn Al-Khatīb (1313–74) and his contemporary Ibn Khātimah, the Spanish-Muslim scholars, who both wrote independently, amongst other works, two of the earliest accounts of the plague or Black Death and deduced its spread as due to contagion.

The Middle Ages both in Asia and Europe were characterized by a widespread faith in astrology and alchemy. The alchemical

[1] Sarton, *op. cit.*, II, p. 1101.

writings of Jabīr ibn Ḥayyan were followed by many others, predominantly mystical and elusive and containing less of real chemistry. Mention may be made, however, of three alchemists of note, namely, Abū-l-Qāsim Al-'Irāqī (second half of the thirteenth century), 'Abdallāh ibn 'Alī Al-Kāshānī (flourished *c.* 1300), and Al-Jildakī (first half of the fourteenth century). Abū-l-Qāsim wrote several alchemical treatises, including the book entitled *Knowledge acquired concerning the Cultivation of Gold*, and on which Al-Jildakī later wrote a commentary. In the theory of *kīmīyā*, of which Abū-l-Qāsim treats, the metals form a series in which the highest member is gold ; they are distinguished by accidental differences, such as more heat or more cold, and are therefore capable of transmutation through the removal of these differences by the philosopher's stone (*al-iksīr*). 'Abdallāh ibn 'Alī Al-Kāshānī is noted for a unique account of the manufacture of faïence or enamelled pottery in mediaeval Persia, the manuscript of which, written in his own hand and dated Tabrīz 1300, was discovered in 1935 in the Library of Hagia Sophia in Istanbul by H. Ritter. Al-Jildakī wrote many treatises, and our study of his alchemical works is incomplete, but he knew how to separate silver from gold in a gold-silver alloy by means of acid, he made the very important statement that substances react chemically by definite weights, and he has left us a brief history of the Arabic alchemists.

The practical arts dependent upon a scientific approach were not neglected by Arabic scholars ; for instance, interest in the beautiful Arab horse led to elaborate treatises on hippology and hippiatry and to a stimulation of veterinary studies generally. The best mediaeval treatise, based upon a wide practical experience of the veterinary art, is the *Kitāb al-Nāṣiri* of Ibn Al-Mundhir, who flourished in Egypt in the first half of the fourteenth century ; other treatises dealing with the horse were written in the second half of the same century by Ibn Juzayy and by his disciple Ibn Hudhail, both of Granada. Again, in agriculture a valuable treatise was written by Al-'Abbās Al-Rasūlī, who was sixth Rasūlī sulṭān of the Yemen between 1362 and 1376. This treatise dealt with soils, fertilizers, waters, the seasons, growth of crops from seed, pulses, cucumber plants such as melons, fruit trees—with particular attention to the date-palm, sugar-cane, cotton, grafting of trees—with illustrations of the instruments, medicinal plants of the Yemen, and other subjects.

Of the later Muslim astronomers and mathematicians may be mentioned Al-Mizzī (d. 1349), who was muezzin of the great mosque at Damascus and who made astrolabes and quadrants about which he wrote in several treatises; Ibn Al-Shāṭir (1306–75), also of Damascus, who invented two new types of quadrant and in his writings criticized the Ptolemaic system of astronomy; and 'Abdallāh ibn Khalīl Al-Mārdīnī (or Maridīnī), (d. *c.* 1407) muezzin in the Omayyad mosque in Damascus, an author of works on the use of quadrants and on trigonometry. There were many such eminent men, mainly Syrian (as was Al-Khalīlī) or Egyptian (as was Ibn Al-Majdī), and they were chiefly occupied in making accurate astronomical instruments (of which some fine examples remain with us) and in determining the exact times of prayer and the location of the *qibla* which specified the direction of Mecca. Amongst the mathematicians were Ibn Al-Hā'im Al-Faraḍī (d. 1412), a professor in the Ṣalāḥīya madrasa (founded by Ṣalāḥ al-Dīn—Saladin—in 1188) in Jerusalem, who wrote many arithmetical and algebraical books; and Ibn Al-Qunfūdh (d. *c.* 1407), the Algerian scholar, who has left an interesting commentary—*Ḥaṭṭ al-niqāb*—on the *Talkhīṣ* of Ibn al-Bannā'. A recent study of manuscripts of the *Ḥaṭṭ al-niqāb* made by H. P. J. Renaud of Rabat has revealed developments in algebraic symbolism.

Ibn Al-Qunfūdh uses the initial letter of the Arabic word *shay'*, a thing, to represent the unknown quantity x, the initial letter of the word *māl*, a square, to represent x^2, the initial letter of *ka'b*, a cube, to represent x^3; together with other initial letters, suitably modified, to represent equality and root; and short words, such as *wa* (and), to represent addition, for other algebraical processes.

We close this brief survey of the Islamic contribution to science by reference to Ulūgh Beg. Ulūgh Beg was the grandson of the terrible Tīmūr Lang who completed in 1401 the destruction of Baghdad begun by Hūlāgū in 1258, and who caused the final ruin of the irrigation system of Tigris-Euphrates which had suffered from gradual neglect since Sassanian times, when it is said "a squirrel could travel from Seleucia to the Persian Gulf without ever having to come to ground". As if to make some recompense for the devastation caused by his grandfather (though Tīmūr encouraged learned men and brought them to Samarkand), Ulūgh Beg established *c.* 1420 the finest astronomical observatory in the world near to the beautiful capital city. Among the astronomers who worked there were Jamshīd ibn Mas'ūd (who made use of decimal fractions), Qāḍī Zāde al-Rūmī, and 'Alī ibn Muḥammad al-Qūshchī; and there resulted from the labours of the observers at Samarkand the famous catalogue of stars called *Zīj Ulūgh Beg* (1437), which had a world-wide influence; a Georgian translation made by Wakhtang VI (*Ḥusain Qulī Khān*) appeared even in the early eighteenth century.

(iii) THE SCIENTIFIC LEGACY OF ISLĀM TO LATIN CHRISTENDOM

This vast store of scientific knowledge which the Muslim world had assimilated from both East and West was augmented, and passed, in the main, to mediaeval European scholars through the intellectual centres in Sicily and in Spain. But many manuscripts remained in the East and their contents were revealed only with the later European penetration of India, when by that time seventeenth-century Europe had of itself made the same discoveries independently; nor is the thrill of finding other manuscripts a thing of the past—indeed, the great mosque libraries of such cities as Istanbul are only just beginning to reveal their scientific secrets, and valuable new information has come to light within recent years.

It was upon this legacy of knowledge from Islām that the Scientific Renaissance of Europe largely grew, the core of knowledge being essentially Greek. Thus the Greek classics of science returned, after many vicissitudes and travels, to Europe, and were supplemented by many observations and commentaries made by the Asiatic world. The Muslim influence in Spain was the result of an occupation of over seven hundred years, and such a long sojourn cannot have failed to produce permanent results. The last Muslims left Spain as Columbus rode the high seas to America, fortified in his endeavours by the knowledge [1] of a spherical earth derived from the Arabic version of the Geography of Ptolemy: such is the universality of science which knows no creeds nor colours, and is the common heritage of mankind.

The European aspects of this transmission of science are outside the province of this little book, but a few observations on its mechanism will not be out of place. Translations were probably often made by three men working together, a Christian, a Muslim, and a Jew who provided the link between them because he knew both Latin and Arabic; the part played by Jewish transmitters is in any case highly important. Work attributed

[1] It seems likely that Columbus also knew of a prior discovery of America by the Portuguese.

to some of the great translators was often done by others working under direction, and the whole process was greatly facilitated by the help and enthusiasm of such patrons of learning as the Emperor Frederick II of Sicily, Alfonso X El Sabio (the Learned) of León and Castile, and the Archbishop Raymond I of Toledo, as we have already noted. Frederick II was instrumental in causing translations of the writings of Aristotle and Ibn Rushd to be made and to be sent to Bologna and Paris, and he posed to Muslim scholars such questions as: Why do oars immersed in water appear bent? Why does Canopus appear larger when near the horizon, even when there is no moisture in the atmosphere? Frederick employed Michael Scot as his astrologer and translator, and had also Muslim advisors. His scientific outlook is clearly revealed in his elaborate zoological work, *A Treatise on Falconry*, which contained new observations relating to the anatomy of birds, and some remarks on migration and on the mechanism of flight; he also made experiments on the artificial incubation of eggs. Alfonso the Learned was instrumental in promoting the translation of Arabic works into Spanish, and for many of these he wrote prefaces; by his order a series of works on astronomy derived from the Arabic were collected and edited *c.* 1276 under the title *Libros del saber de astronomia* and comprised in encyclopaedic form all that was known to him concerning the construction and use of astronomical instruments. Some four years earlier Alfonso had also issued the *Alphonsine Tables*, prepared at Toledo by Judah ben Moses and Isaac ibn Sid, which replaced the *Toledan Tables* of Al-Zarqālī, so that his interest in astronomy was a very live one and did not confine itself merely to transmission of existing texts, valuable though this was to be to Europe subsequently. Toledo was the centre of translation in Spain, and it was here in the previous century, under Raymond I, who was Archbishop from 1126 to

1151, that active co-operation in the transmission of knowledge had begun; translations were frequently made from Arabic into Castilian, and the work was completed by a further translation by those who knew Castilian and Latin. Sometimes there were partnerships of two men working together, as, for example, John of Seville, a converted Jew, and Domingo Gundisalvo. The process of transmission was not a simple one, as may be readily seen; it was beset with difficulties and took much labour and time, and the Latin version, if it emerged at all, did so often after long delay: many translations never appeared in Spanish, but were made into Portuguese or Hebrew versions; again, whilst Toledo and Palermo were the foci of intellectual effort, translations were also made in Syria during the Crusades, and—when the Greek originals became available, directly into Latin by translators in northern Italy.

Amongst the famous translators of the twelfth century were Adelard of Bath, who rendered from Arabic into Latin (1) *The Elements of Euclid*, and (2) Al-Majrīṭī's revision of the astronomical tables of Al-Khuwārizmī, thus introducing trigonometry to Europe; the above-mentioned John of Seville and his collaborator Gundisalvo, who produced Latin versions of the astronomy of Al-Farghānī and of philosophical works by Al-Fārābī, Ibn Sīnā, and Al-Ghazzālī; Robert of Chester, the first man to produce a Latin translation of (1) *The Qur'ān*, and (2) The Algebra of Al-Khuwārizmī, thus initiating the study of algebra in Europe; Gerard of Cremona (Gherardo Cremonese), perhaps the greatest of all the translators, who worked and directed others with such stupendous energy at Toledo that the output of his "school" is incredible—certainly he himself could not have performed the task unaided. Gerard made an independent translation from Arabic to Latin of Euclid's *Elements*, based upon Thābit ibn Qurra; of the *Almagest* of Ptolemy, which was completed at Toledo in 1175, printed at Venice in 1515, and had great influence in western Europe; and of the *Qānūn* of Ibn Sīnā, which determined the medical studies in the famous Italian universities such as Milan and Padua; in addition, versions were made of many of the writings of Aristotle and of both the Greek and Arabic mathematicians. In the thirteenth century were Samuel ibn Tibbon (*c.* 1150–*c.* 1232), who made translations from Arabic to Hebrew (e.g. of Aristotle's *Meteorology*); Jacob Anaṭoli, who worked in the same languages and translated Ptolemy's *Almagest*; the scholars who studied under the patronage of Alfonso X El Sabio; Moses ibn Tibbon, who flourished *c.* 1240–83, and made many translations from Arabic to Hebrew, including those of Aristotle's *De anima*, Euclid's *Elements*, and certain medical treatises of Ibn Sīnā and Al-Rāzī; and Jacob ben Maḥir ibn Tibbon, the astronomer and grandson of Samuel ibn Tibbon, also a translator from Arabic to Hebrew, who produced versions of the *Data* and the *Elements* of Euclid, the *Spherics* of Menelaos, and the *Fī hai'at al-'ālam* (*Configuration of the World*) of Al-Haitham. The fourteenth century also claimed an eminent translator of Arabic works into Hebrew, namely, Qalonymos ben Qalonymos, who made versions of some of the writings of Archimedes, Galen, Jābir, Al-Kindī, and Al-Fārābī. But Jewish scholars are not noted only for their translations. Valuable original work was done, for instance, by Levi ben Gerson (1288–1344), a Judeo-Provençal philosopher and mathematician, who invented the cross-staff to measure the angular elevation of the sun.

Through this complex process of transmission certain practical operations of science became known to western Europe as a result of the earlier researches of such men as Jābir, the chemist, and Al-Haitham, the physicist. Also the directive property of the magnetic needle, though it was probably a Chinese discovery of the eleventh century, was used in navigation by the Muslim seamen, who brought the knowledge to the Mediterranean; and the compass seems to have been well known in the time of Alexander Neckam, the Englishman (d. 1217) who speaks of it. Islamic science also brought a valuable technical terminology to the West, especially in chemistry and astronomy. Words such as alcohol and azimuth are but two of many. The process of transmission is sometimes revealed in an interesting manner by the words, e.g. as we have already noted in Chapter IV, the Sanskrit term *jyā*, meaning bow or curve, was transformed to the Arabic *jaib* (a bay or curved inlet), whence it became *sinus* (a curve) with Robert of Chester, and sine with us to-day. Finally, we may credit Islām with the development of hospitals and the spread of their influence, though the first efforts were Byzantine, and inspired by Christianity. The wider conception derived from the great Sassanian medical school of Gundīshapūr, which survived the Muslim conquest of Persia in the seventh century, and continued to flourish alongside Baghdad. This wider conception came to practical fruition in the great non-clerical institutions such as the Bīmāristān al-Manṣūrī (Qalā'ūn's Hospital) in Cairo, built in the latter part of the thirteenth century and still partly extant.

Looking back we may say that Islamic medicine and science reflected the light of the Hellenic sun, when its day had fled, and that they shone like a moon, illuminating the darkest night of the European Middle Ages; that some bright stars lent their own light, and that moon and stars alike faded at the dawn of a new day—the Renaissance. Since they had their share in the direction and introduction of that great movement, it may reasonably be claimed that they are with us yet.[1]

[1] Max Meyerhof in *Legacy of Islam*, Clarendon Press, Oxford, p. 354.

5. *MODERN TIMES: WHAT ASIAN SCIENCE TEACHES US*

With the Renaissance of science in Europe in the sixteenth and seventeenth centuries the initiative passed from the East to the West, and the last three hundred years have witnessed a progress in science and technology which has been essentially European. In the East, however, certain singular advances have been made, and having been overshadowed by the far greater Western contribution, have attracted insufficient notice: of these advances two will be briefly discussed, namely, the astronomical researches inspired by Jai Singh in India, and the unique development of the theory of determinants, a branch of higher algebra, by the Japanese.

The Hindu Mahārāja Sawāī Jai Singh II of Jaipur (A.D. 1686–1743) made an impartial study of Muslim, Hindu, and European astronomical methods, and built observatories at Delhi, Jaipur, Ujjain, Benares, and Mathurā. Jai Singh was familiar with Euclid's *Elements of Geometry*, Ptolemy's *Almagest*, certain writings on the astrolabe, the *Tables* of Ulūgh Beg of Samarkand, the *Tabulae Astronomicae* of P. de la Hire, and Flamsteed's *Historia Coelestis Britannica*: he also understood the principles of spherical trigonometry and of logarithms. His chief astronomer was a Hindu named Jagannāth, who was employed by Jai Singh to make translations into Sanskrit of Euclid's *Elements* and Ptolemy's *Almagest* from the Arabic versions existing; his Muslim assistants facilitated the understanding of Arabic star catalogues and the copying of the instruments used by Ulūgh Beg at Samarkand; whilst the sending by Jai Singh of Padre Manuel and others to Europe *c.* 1728, and the visit of Father Boudier to Jaipur in 1734, effected European contacts.

Jai Singh set himself three tasks: (1) to absorb as much as possible of the astronomical information of his predecessors, whether Asian or European; (2) to improve astronomical measuring instruments and erect efficient observatories; (3) to compile a better set of astronomical tables, rectify the calendar, and predict eclipses more accurately. In spite of the troubled times in which he lived, Jai Singh was successful in effecting extensive and valuable observations, and though no new discoveries were made, the astronomical tables of Ulūgh Beg were brought up to date.

The instruments used were the sun-dial (*Naḍi Yantra*), the sphere (*Gola Yantra*), the azimuth instrument (*Digaṁśa Yantra*), the mural quadrant (*Dakhshino Digbhitt*), the equinoctial dial (*Samrāṭ Yantra*), the hemispherical dial (*Jaya Prakāś*), and the 60° arc or sextant (*Vṛitta Shashtāmśaka*), which was placed in the meridian. We learn something of this observational work in the preface to the *Zīj Muḥammad Shāhī*: [1]

He (Jai Singh) found that the calculation of the places of the stars as obtained from the tables in common use . . . in very many cases gives them as widely different from those determined by observation: especially in the appearance of the new moons, the computation does not agree with observation. . . .

Although this [revision] was a mighty task, which during a long period of time none of the powerful Rajas had prosecuted; nor among the tribes of Islām, since the time of the martyr prince, whose sins are forgiven, Mirza Ulugh Beg, to the present, which comprehends a period of more than three hundred years, had any one of the kings possessed of power and dignity turned his attention to this object. Yet to accomplish the exalted command he had received, he bound the girdle of resolution about the loins of his soul and constructed here [at

[1] The astronomical tables of Jai Singh, named after the Emperor Muḥammad Shāh.

Delhi] several of the instruments of an observatory, such as had been erected at Samarqand, agreeable to the Mussulman books, such as Zāt al-Halqa [armillary sphere] of brass, in diameter three gaz [perhaps 9 feet] of the measure now in use, and Zāt al-Sha'batain [regulae parallacticae or astrolabe of two rings], and Zāt al-Zaqatain and Sads Fakhri [Vṛitta Shashtāmśaka] and Shāmalah [Jai Prakāś].

But finding that brass instruments did not come up to the ideas which he had formed of accuracy, because of the smallness of their size, the want of division into minutes, the shaking and wearing of their axes, the displacement of the centres of the circles, and the shifting of the planes of the instruments, he concluded that the reason why the determinations of the ancients, such as Hipparchus and Ptolemy, proved inaccurate, must have been of this kind.

Therefore he constructed in Dār al-Kalafat Shāh Jahānābād [Delhi], which is the seat of empire and prosperity, instruments of his own invention, such as Jai Prakāś and Rām Yantra [1] and Samrāṭ Yantra, the semi-diameter of which is of eighteen cubits, and one minute on it is a barley corn and a half—of stone and lime of perfect stability, with attention to the rules of geometry and adjustment to the meridian and to the latitude of the place, and with care in the measuring and fixing of them, so that the inaccuracies from the shaking of the circles and the wearing of their axes and displacement of their centres and the inequality of the minutes might be corrected. Thus an accurate method of constructing an observatory was established, and the difference which had existed between the computed and observed places of the fixed stars and planets by means of observing their mean motions and observations was removed. . . . On examining and comparing the calculations of these tables [the tables of P. de la Hire and of earlier European astronomers] with actual observations it appeared that there was an error in the former [i.e. of De La Hire] in assigning the moon's place of half a degree. Although the error in the other planets was not so

[1] The *Rām Yantra*, constructed of stone, was cylindrical, open at the top, and had a pillar at its centre. The interior was graduated to permit azimuth and altitude observations.

great, yet the times of solar and lunar eclipses he found to come out later or earlier than the truth by the fourth part of a ghaṭi or fifteen palas [1 ghaṭi = 60 palas = 24 minutes]. Hence he concluded that, since in Europe astronomical instruments have not been constructed of such a size and so large diameters, the motions which have been observed with them may have deviated a little from the truth. . . .[1]

Jai Singh was most influenced by the Muslim tradition of astronomy as exemplified in Ulūgh Beg; he was essentially practical in outlook, and paid considerable attention to the astrolabe, an instrument which had been skilfully developed by earlier Arabic observers. His great work came to fruition especially in 1724, when the Delhi observatory was completed (some forty years after Greenwich), and in 1728 when his astronomical tables—the *Zīj Muḥammad Shāhī*—appeared. Many of the great masonry instruments of Jai Singh remain to-day as monuments to his industry, but the development of the telescope in Europe rapidly opened up other fields in observational astronomy and led to a more elaborate technique. When he died in 1743 "his wives, concubines, and science expired with him on his funeral pyre".

The Japanese mathematicians developed the theory of determinants before European scholars, and quite independently of them. The original interest seems to have been inspired by the Chinese, who, as we have already seen (Chapter 2), were able to solve linear simultaneous equations. The first Japanese treatise was the *Fukudai* written by Seki Kōwa in 1683, and in his elimination of an arbitrary quantity from two equations containing it (the use to which the Japanese invariably put their determinant theory), he displayed an elegance of method equal or perhaps finer than that of Sylvester in England two centuries

[1] Quotations from Hunter, *Asiatic Researches*, V, pp. 178 f. (1799). This is his translation of the preface of the *Zīj Muḥammad Shāhī*.

later. The work was developed by Seki's successors and a general rule is to be found in an anonymous treatise, *Taisei Sankyō*. The Japanese were primarily concerned with the process of elimination of unrequired quantities from their equations, and do not appear to have used their determinants with the specific object of solving simultaneous equations. Thus, taking an *extremely* simple case of the two equations

$$a_1 + a_2x = 0 \quad . \quad . \quad . \quad . \quad (1)$$

and

$$b_1 + b_2x = 0 \quad . \quad . \quad . \quad . \quad (2)$$

elimination of x is effected by multiplying (1) by b_2 and (2) by a_2 and subtracting, i.e.

$$a_1b_2 + a_2b_2x = 0$$

$$a_2b_1 + a_2b_2x = 0,$$

giving

$$a_1b_2 - a_2b_1 = 0\,;$$

and this may be written in *modern* form as the determinant

$$\begin{vmatrix} a_1 & a_2 \\ b_1 & b_2 \end{vmatrix}$$

which may be evaluated by multiplying in the way indicated by the arrows:

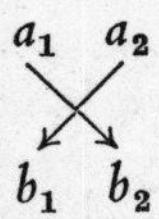

This oblique multiplication (*shajō*) gave rise to positive terms such as a_1b_2 (*sei*, creative), and negative terms such as $-a_2b_1$ (*koku*, destructive), since in the latter case multiplication is in a different sense. A good description of shajō was given in 1798 by Kwanno Genken in his *Hoi Kai Fukudai Sei Koku Hen*.

It should be remembered that Seki and his successors dealt

with equations of a *much* greater difficulty than this, and that the general rule was soon arrived at for two equations such as

$$a_1 + a_2x + a_3x^2 + a_4x^3 + \ldots + a_nx^{n-1} = 0$$

and $$b_1 + b_2x + b_3x^2 + b_4x^3 + \ldots + b_nx^{n-1} = 0,$$

where n is *any* number.

The Japanese notation for the determinant was of the form

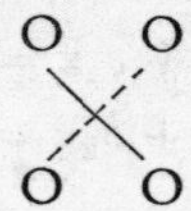

terms joined by a dotted red line leading to a positive product and those joined by a full black line leading to a negative product, the sense being opposite to that of the modern form. The colours recall the Chinese system of *k'ien yüan shu* (Chapter 2). The whole determinant follows so easily from the elegant Chinese and Japanese method of writing equations, and begins from the top with the constant term, thus denoting the powers by their *position*, e.g. :—

c_1	b_1	a_1
c_2	b_2	a_2
c_3	b_3	a_3
c_4	b_4	a_4
c_5	b_5	a_5

represents $$a_1 + a_2x + a_3x^2 + a_4x^3 + a_5x^4 = 0,$$
$$b_1 + b_2x + b_3x^2 + b_4x^3 + b_5x^4 = 0,$$
and $$c_1 + c_2x + c_3x^2 + c_4x^3 + c_5x^4 = 0.$$

Japanese progress in the theory of determinants can be traced through the *Yendon kai Fukudai no Hō of Seki Kōwa* (1683), the *Sampō Hakki* of Izeki Chishin printed at Osaka in 1690, the *Kai Fukudai Kōshiki Shajō no Genkai* (1715)—perhaps by Matsunaga Ryōhitsu, the *Kyūshi Ikō* containing results obtained by Kurushima Gita, the *Sei-koku Impō Den* of Toita Yasusuke (1759), the *Kaihō Yōshi* of Arima Raidō, who was a feudal lord of Kurume in Kyūshū (1762), and the *Hoi Kai Fukudai Sei-koku Hen* of Kwanno Genken (1798). The works of Kurushima and of Kwanno, if examined together, would reveal that the value of a determinant is not altered by changing the rows into columns and the columns into rows, a generalization which neither saw from his own individual researches. Yosiho Mikami has written :

> If the determinants theory, thus far advanced in Japan during the 17th and 18th centuries, had continued to be cared for some time longer, it would no doubt have undergone a wonderful progress, but such was not the case. From the beginning of the 19th century onward, it was destined to be gradually neglected, and curiously enough, in the closing days of the old Japanese school of mathematics it was forgotten altogether.[1]

More recent scientific researches in the East have naturally been largely influenced by the trend of European science, e.g. in the early years of the present century, the widespread interest in atomic structure and the origin of light resulted in a 'model' of the atom devised by Nagaoka in Japan and some brilliant researches by Sir C. V. Raman on optical spectra. But there have also been some results of peculiar and individual genius, such as those derived from the researches of Sir J. C. Bose on the sensitive reactions and physiological processes of the living plant, and of S. Ramanujan in higher mathematical thought.

[1] *Isis*, II, 35.

It will be immediately perceived from this short survey of the history of science as it especially concerns Asia that from the practice of scientific research there grows a body of knowledge which is cumulative, and being objective (as far as human knowledge can be so) it becomes also international, in that it is the common property of all the men from all the races who have experimented with and thought about natural phenomena without bias; for with bias, personal or national, objective scientific truth becomes impossible.

Certain fundamental ideas are common to thinkers of all races and have occurred from time to time in both hemispheres, e.g. the atomic theory is to be found both in Greek and Jaina philosophy. It is simply that when the keener minds meditate upon cosmogony and cosmology, a monism or a dualism in some form or other emerges. Nor is 'the ether' a new creation: Homer thought about it.

Further, the body of scientific knowledge has progressed through four stages, alternately Eastern, then Western; the Ancient Empires of the East passed their rudimentary science to Greece, which in turn bequeathed to the care of the East a new science strengthened by proof and generalization; this, in turn, by the stupendous labours of many translators, passed from Islām to Latin Christendom, during the latter half of the millennium of gestation which preceded the re-birth of science in Europe. Though the two European phases are admittedly the greater, the picture is incomplete without the two Asian ones. Moreover, what Asia has lacked in science she has amply compensated for by her genius in other directions, e.g. in religion.

Finally, the study of the history of science in the East enables the Western student to see science, and especially technology, in its true setting. Though Asian peoples are being rapidly caught up in the materialistic advance of the West they have a deep well of spiritual inspiration from which they may draw and to which their poets continually return. We feel it, for instance, with Rabindranath Tagore in his reverence for the Upanishads, and in the penetrating studies of Buddhist psychology made by Lafcadio Hearn, a Westerner who fell in love with the old Japan. The interpretation of Nature by Western science is but one interpretation. On gazing at the moon on a soft tropical night, the observer may be inclined towards a desire to measure the height of its mountains from the shadows cast over its surface by them, as Galileo did in his day, but so strong is the emotion in man and so weak his rationalism, that he will probably, as in Hindu mythology, associate her with the essenc of a beautiful woman. So there have always been ‘ digits of the moon ’, and very few scientists because they are too critical ; and science has had to fight for recognition over the centuries, and historians (who often prefer feeling to fact) have only recently discovered, with the increasing pressure of a technical civilization, that science has a history which is worthy of record. Of the Asian aspects of this history we know comparatively little.

SELECT BIBLIOGRAPHY

1. The Ancient Civilizations

G. Sarton. *Introduction to the History of Science*, Vol. I. Baltimore, 1927.

Abel Rey. *La Science Orientale avant les Grecs.* Paris, 1930.

J. L. Heiberg. *Geschichte der Mathematik und Naturwissenschaften in Altertum.* München, 1925.

C. P. S. Menon. *Ancient Astronomy and Cosmology.* London, 1931.

P. Tannery. *Recherches sur l'histoire de l'astronomie ancienne.* Paris, 1893.

C. L. Woolley. *The Sumerians.* Oxford, 1929.

F. Thureau-Dangin. *Textes mathématiques Babyloniens.* Leiden, 1938.

O. Neugebauer and A. J. Sachs. *Mathematical Cuneiform Texts.* American Oriental Series No. 29, New Haven, Conn., 1945.

Ch. Virolleaud. *L'Astrologie Chaldéenne.* Paris, 1908–12.

E. F. Weidner. *Handbuch der babylonischen Astronomie*, I. Leipzig, 1915.

R. C. Thompson. *On the Chemistry of the Ancient Assyrians.* London, 1925.

R. C. Thompson. *The Assyrian Herbal.* London, 1925.

M. Jastrow. "The Medicine of the Babylonians and Assyrians", *Proc. Roy. Soc. Medicine* (Section, Hist. of Medicine), VII, pp. 109–76. London, 1914.

J. H. Breasted. *The Edwin Smith Surgical Papyrus.* 2 vols. Chicago, 1930.

T. E. Peet. *The Rhind Mathematical Papyrus.* London, 1923.

S. R. K. Glanville (edited by). *The Legacy of Egypt.* Oxford, 1942. (Articles by Sloley, Warren Dawson, Engelbach, and Sewell.)

Sir J. Marshall. *Mohenjo-Daro and the Indus Civilisation*, 3 vols. London, 1931.

G. T. Garrett (edited by). *The Legacy of India.* Oxford, 1937. (*Vide* articles by F. W. Thomas, de B. Codrington, S. N. Das Gupta, and W. E. Clark.)

G. N. Banerjee. *Hellenism in Ancient India.* 2nd edn. Calcutta, 1920.

A. F. R. Hoernle. *Studies in the Medicine of Ancient India.* London, 1907.

Bibhutibhusan Datta. *The Science of the Śulba.* Calcutta, 1932.

L. de Saussure. *Les origines de l'astronomie chinoise.* (T'oung Pao, X–XII, XIV, XV, XXI.) Leyden, 1909–14. In book form, Paris, 1930.

J. Needham. *Science and Society in Ancient China* (Conway Memorial Lecture). London, 1947.

J. Needham. *Natural Law in China and in Europe.* Journal of Hist. of Ideas, Vol. XII 1 and 2.

G. Thibaut. "On the Sūryaprajñapti", *Journ. Asiatic Soc. of Bengal,* XLIX, pp. 107–27, 181–206 (1880).

G. Schiaperelli. *L'Astronomia nell' Antico Testamento.* Milano, 1903.

2. Mediaeval China

J. Needham. *Science and Civilization in China.* (To appear.)

A. Stein. *Innermost Asia.* 4 vols. Oxford, 1928.

G. Sarton. *Introduction to the History of Science,* 3 vols., Baltimore, 1927–48.

Lynn Thorndike. *A History of Magic and Experimental Science.* 6 vols. New York, 1923–41.

K. C. Wong and Lien-Teh Wu. *History of Chinese Medicine.* Tientsin, 1932. 2nd ed., Shanghai, 1936.

T. F. Carter. *The Invention of Printing in China and its spread Westwards.* New York, 1925.

A. Forke. *The World Conception of the Chinese.* London, 1925.

H. Yule. *The Book of Ser. Marco Polo.* 2 vols. London, 1903. Reprint 1926.

M. C. Johnson. "Greek, Moslem, and Chinese Instrument Design in the surviving Mongol Equatorials of 1279 A.D.", *Isis,* Vol. XXXII, pp. 27–43, 1947.

H. Chatley. "Ancient China", *Engineering,* Feb. 27, 1942.

J. Needham. *The Unity of Science: Asia's Indispensable Contribution.* UNESCO Lecture, Beirut, 1948. Archives Internat. d'Hist. des Sciences, II 566, 1949.

Li Ch'iao-p'ing. "The Chemical Arts of Old China", *Jour. Chem. Educ.* Easton, Pennsylvania.

3. Mediaeval India

G. Thibaut and Sudharkar Dvivedi. *The Pañchasiddhāntikā of Varāhamihira.* Benares, 1889.

E. Sachau (edited by). *Al Beruni's India. An account . . . of India about* A.D. 1030. New edit., 2 vols. London, 1910.

Ph. Gangooly and P. Sengupta. *Sūrya Siddhānta* (Burgess). Calcutta, 1935.

G. R. Kaye. *Indian Mathematics.* Calcutta and Simla, 1915.

G. T. Garratt (edited by). *Legacy of India.* Oxford, 1937.

W. E. Clark. *The Āryabhatīya of Āryabbata.* Chicago, 1930.

H. T. Colebrooke. *Algebra, with Arithmetic and Mensuration from the Sanskrit of Brahmagupta and Bhaskara.* London, 1817.

B. Datta and A. N. Singh. *History of Hindu Mathematics : A Source Book.* Lahore, 1938.

G. R. Kaye. The Bakhshālī Manuscript. *Archaeological Survey of India,* Vol. XLII. Calcutta, 1927.

D. E. Smith and L. C. Karpinski. *The Hindu-Arabic Numerals.* New York, 1911.

A. F. R. Hoernle. The Bower Manuscript. *Archaeological Survey of India,* Vol. XXII. Calcutta, 1893.

A. F. R. Hoernle. *Studies in the Medicine of Ancient India.* Oxford, 1907.

Sir P. C. Rāy. *A History of Hindu Chemistry.* 2 vols. Calcutta, 1902, 1909.

4. The Scope of Arabic Science

(i)

Sir Thomas Arnold and A. Guillaume. *The Legacy of Islam.* Oxford, 1931. (Articles by M. Meyerhof and Baron Carra de Vaux.)

T. Houtsma and others. *Encyclopaedia of Islam.* Leiden, 1906–34. Supplement, 1938.

C. Brockelmann. *Geschichte der Arabischen Literatur.* 2 vols. Weimar-Berlin, 1898–1902. Supplement, Leiden, 1937.

G. Jacob. *Studien in Arabischen Geographen.* 2 vols. Berlin, 1891–2.

A. Mieli and others. *La science arabe et son rôle dans l'évolution scientifique.* Leiden, 1939.

A. Mingana. *Job of Edessa's Book of Treasures.* Cambridge, 1935.

J. Ruska. *Griechische Planetendarstellungen in arabischen Steinbuchern.* Heidelberg, 1919.

J. Ruska. *Zur ältesten arabischen Algebra und Rechenkunst.* Heidelberg, 1917.

G. Sarton. *Introduction to the History of Science.* 3 vols. Baltimore, 1927–48.

(ii)

Carra de Vaux. *Penseurs d'Islam.* Vol. II. Paris, 1923.

P. Kraus. *Jābir ibn Ḥayyān.* 2 vols. Cairo, 1942–3.

E. J. Holmyard. *The Works of Geber, Englished by Richard Russell,* 1678. London, New York, 1928.

H. E. Stapleton, R. F. Azo, and Ḥidāyat Ḥusain. *Chemistry in 'Iraq and Persia in the Tenth Century* A.D. Mem. Asiatic Soc., Bengal. Calcutta, 1927.

G. Le Strange. *Baghdad during the 'Abbāsid Caliphate, from Contemporary Arabic and Persian Sources.* Oxford, 1924.

L. C. Karpinski. *Robert of Chester's Latin Translation of the Algebra of Al-Khuwarizmi.* New York, 1915.

E. G. Browne. *Arabian Medicine.* Cambridge, 1921.

D. Campbell. *Arabian Medicine.* 2 vols. London, 1926.

M. Meyerhof. *The Book of the Ten Treatises on the Eye ascribed to Ḥunayn ibn Isḥāq.* Cairo, 1928.

G. Bergstrasser. *Ḥunain ibn Isḥāk und seine Schule.* Leiden, 1913.

Flügel, Rödinger and A. Müller. *Kitāb al-Fihrist.* Leipzig, 1872.

C. E. Sachau. *Chronologie orientalischer Volker (al-Bīrūnī).* Leipzig, 1876–8. English version, London, 1879.

Carra de Vaux. *Avicenne.* Paris, 1900.

Mustafā Nazīf Bey. *Al-Ḥasan ibn Al-Haitham.* 2 vols, in Arabic. Cairo, 1942–3.

F. Woepke. *L'Algèbre d'Umar Khayyâmi.* Paris, 1851.

D. S. Kasir. *The Algebra of Omar Khayyām.* New York, 1931.

H. J. J. Winter and W. 'Arafat. "The Algebra of 'Umar Khayyām", *Jour. Roy. Asiatic Soc. Bengal,* Vol. XVI. Calcutta, 1950.

A. Müller. *Ibn Abi Usaibi'a.* 2 vols. Königsberg, 1884.

W. Hartner. Article on the astrolabe, in *Survey of Persian Art.* (A. U. Pope.) Vol. III, Chap. 57. Oxford, 1939.

A. Jourdain. *Mémoire sur l'observatoire de Méragah . . .* Paris, 1810.

H. Suter. *Die Mathematiker und Astronomen der Araber.* Leipzig, 1900.

L. A. Sedillot. *Prolégomènes des tables astronomiques d'Olough-Beg, etc.* Paris, 1847.

E. G. Browne. *Chahār Maqāla.* 2 vols. London, 1910.

Q. H. Tuqan. *The Scientific Heritage of the Arabs in Mathematics and Astronomy.* In Arabic. Cairo, 1941.

E. Wiedemann. *Beiträge zur Geschichte der Naturwissenschaften,* 69 parts. Erlangen, 1904–29. In *Sitzungsberichte d. phys. w. med. Soc.*

C. Schoy. "Beiträge zur Arabischen Trigonometrie", *Isis,* V, 364–99, 1923.

C. A. Nallino. *Raccolta di Scritti editi e inediti.* Vol. 5. Roma, 1944.

(iii)

C. H. Haskins. *Studies in the History of Mediaeval Science.* Harvard, 1924.

M. Steinschneider. *Die Europäischen Uebersetzungen aus dem Arabischen bis Mitte des 17 Jahrhunderts.* 2 parts. Vienna, 1904–5.

M. Steinschneider. *Die hebräischen Übersetzungen des Mittelalters.* Berlin, 1893.

R. Walzer. *Arabic Transmission of Greek Thought to Mediaeval Europe.* Bulletin of the Rylands Library, Manchester, 1945.

J. A. Sanchez Pérez. *Biografías de matemáticos árabes que florecieron en España.* Madrid, 1921.

Manuel Rico y Sinobas. *Libros del saber de Astronomia del rey D. Alfonso X de Castilla.* Madrid, 1863–7.

J. Millas Vallicrosa. *Neuvas aportaciones para el estudio de las transmisíon de la ciencia a Europa a través de España.* Barcelona, 1943.

5. Modern Times

G. R. Kaye. "The Astronomical Observatories of Jai Singh", *Archaeological Survey of India*, Vol. XL. Calcutta, 1918.

D. E. Smith and Y. Mikami. *History of Japanese Mathematics.* Chicago, 1911.

Yoshio Mikami. *The Development of Mathematics in China and Japan.* Leipzig, 1913.

T. Endō. *History of Japanese Mathematics* (in Japanese). Tōkyō, 1896. Revised edition by Y. Mikami and others. Tōkyō, 1918.

BRIEF INDEX

Abacus, 29
'Abbāsid, 61, 62, 69, 79
Abū'l-Faraj (Barhebraeus), 78
Abū'l Jūd, 71
Abū'l-Qāsim (Albucasis), 70
Abū'l-Qāsim Al-'Irāqī, 83
Abū'l Wafā', 69
Adelard of Bath, 67, 88
Afghanistan, 69, 70
Agriculture, 19, 84
Ahmes Papyrus, 11
Akkadian, 6
Al-Battānī (Albategnius), 58, 67
Al-Bīrūnī, 37, 39, 62, 70, 71, 73
Alchemy, Arabic, 64, 65
Alchemy, Chinese, 24, 28
Alexander the Great, 17
Alexandria, 11, 13, 38, 42, 60, 65
Al-Fārābī, 68, 71, 88, 89
Al-Farghānī, 67, 88
Al-Fārisī, 78, 81
Al-Fazārī, 64
Alfonso X (El Sabio), 62, 87, 89
Algebra, Japanese, 94–97
Algebraic notation, 85, 96
Al-Ghazzālī, 88
Al-Ḥakam, 62, 69, 70
Al-Ḥākim, 70
Al-Ḥasan Al-Marrākushī, 78
Al-Haitham (Alhazen), 70, 72, 73, 89
Al-Jazarī, 76
Al-Jildakī, 83
Al-Kāshānī, 83
Al-Khalīlī, 84
Al-Khāzin, 71
Al-Khāzinī, 75
Al-Khuwārizmī, 64, 66, 88
Al-Kindī, 65, 89
Al-Kūhī, 71
Almagest (Syntaxis), 78, 80, 88, 89, 91
Al-Māhānī, 71, 74
Al-Majrīṭī, 67, 88
Al-Ma'mūn, 61, 65, 66
Al-Manṣūr, 61, 64
Al-Mārdīnī (Maridīnī), 84
Al-Mas'ūdī, 69
Al-Mizzī, 84
Almohade, 76
Al-Nadīm, 75
Al-Naubakht, 64
Al-Qūshchī, 85
Al-Rasūlī, 84
Al-Rāzī (Rhazes), 67, 68, 77, 89
Al-Rūmī, Qāḍī Zāde, 85
Al-Shādhilī, 82
Al-Sijzī, 71
Al-Ṭūsī (Nāṣir Al-Dīn), 78–80
Al-'Urdī, 78, 79
Al-Zarqālī, 70, 87
'Amōṣ, 22
Anaesthesia, 30
Anaṭoli, Jacob, 89
Āpastamba, 17
Arab horses, 83
Arabic astronomy, 67, 70, 78
Arabic chemistry, 64, 65
Arabic mathematics, 63, 74, 78
Arabic medicine, 68, 70, 76, 77
Arabic numerals, 56
Archimedes, 74, 75, 80, 89
Area of triangle, 13
Arima Raidō, 97
Aristarchos, 80
Aristotle, 68, 71, 76, 89

Armillary sphere, 79, 93
Artesian wells, 71
Āryabhaṭa I, 39, 46
Āryabhaṭa II, 45, 47
Ashur-bani-pal, 10
Aśoka, 17
Assyrian chemistry, 10
Assyriologists, 6
Asthma, 77
Astrolabe, 70, 78, 84, 91, 93
Astronomy, Babylonian, 9, 10, 38
Astronomy, Chinese, 19, 23, 30, 33–35
Astronomy, Hindu, 30, 37–46
Astronomy, Jaina, 22
Asyut, 15
Athens, 60
Atomic theory, 98
Ātreya, 17
Avantī, 40
Avenzoar, 76, 77
Averroës (Ibn Rushd), 62, 76, 87
Avicenna (Ibn Sīnā), 62, 70–73, 88

Babylonian astronomy, 9, 10, 38
Babylonian mathematics, 8, 12, 15, 56
Babylonian medicine, 12
Bacon, Roger, 72
Baghdad, 61, 62, 64, 65, 68, 69, 85, 90
Bakhshālī Manuscript, 54, 55
Balance, 14, 29, 65, 75
Banū Mūsā, 65, 75, 80
Barhebraeus, 78
Baṣra, 69, 72
Baudhāyana, 17
Benares (Kāśī), 17, 91
Beri-beri, 31
Bhāskara, 46–48, 51, 53
Bīja-Ganita, 48, 49, 51, 54
Bīmāristān, 82, 90
Black Death, 82
Bologna, 62, 87
Bonacosa, 77
Bose, Sir J. C., 97
Botany, 31, 78
Boudier, Father, 91
Bower Manuscript, 58
Brahmagupta, 38, 39, 45, 46, 51, 53
Brahmagupta's Theorem, 47
Brahmagupta's Trapezium, 47
Brāhmaṇas, 6, 17
Brahmasphuṭa-Siddhānta, 38
Brethren of Sincerity (Ikhwān al-Ṣafā'), 69
Bronze, 16, 33
Brouncker, 53, 54
Buddhism, 17, 22, 25, 28, 50, 57
Bukhārā, 71
Burgess, Rev. E., 44
Byzantium, 65, 75, 90

Cairo, 61, 72, 77
Calendar, 9, 15, 19, 34, 70, 92
Camera obscura, 73, 81
Canon of Medicine (*Qānūn*), 71
Carra de Vaux, 56
Castilian, 88
Causation, 23, 25, 26
Cha-Ma-Li-Ting, 34
Chandragupta, 17
Chang Ch'iu-Chien Suan Ching, 51
Chang Chung-Ching, 30
Chang-Ts'ang, 29
Ch'ao Yüan-Fang, 30
Chatley, H., 19
Chaulmoogra oil, 31
Chemistry, Assyrian, 10
Chemistry, Egyptian, 28
Ch'en Tzu-Ming, 31
Chester-Beatty Papyrus, 10
Chia Tan, 31
Ch'ien Han Shu, 24
Ch'in Chiu-shao, 34
Chinese alchemy, 24, 28

Chinese astronomy, 19, 23, 30, 33–35
Chinese botany, 31
Chinese mathematics, 14, 29, 34, 35, 43, 94
Chinese technology, 36
Ching-Li, 32
Chiu Chang Suan Shu, 29, 30
Chiu Huang Pên Ts'ao, 31
CHOSROES I, 43, 60
Chou, 19
Christendom, 61, 85, 98
Chuang-Tzŭ, 23
CHU HSI, 33
CHU SHIH-CHIEH, 34
CHU TAN-CH'I, 31
CH'Ü-T'AN HSI-TA, 30, 57
CHOU WANG TING, 31
Circle, 9, 18, 34, 35, 46, 47, 57
CLARK, W. E., 45, 56
Clepsydra, 10, 19, 39, 42
COLEBROOKE, H. T., 45, 48, 49, 51, 53
COLUMBUS, 86
Completion of the square, 66, 67
Computing rods, 34
Confucianism, 22, 27
Conic sections, 71, 73, 74
Continens, 68
Cordova, 60–62, 69, 70, 76, 77
Cross-staff, 89
Crusades, 88
CTESIBIUS, 36
Cuneiform, 12
Cyclic method, 53

D'ALEMBERT, 50
Damascus, 61, 76, 78, 84
DA VINCI, LEONARDO, 72, 81
De Aspectibus, 65
Decimal system, 29, 30, 34, 85
Dekans, 15
Delhi, 58, 91, 93
DEMOKRITOS, 26
Demotic, 12
DESCARTES, 74, 81
Determinants, 35, 50, 94–97
Dhamma, 23, 25
Diamond Sūtra, 32
DIOPHANTOS, 13, 50, 51
DIOSCORIDES, 11, 68
Dissection, 11

Ebers Papyrus, 10, 11
Edwin Smith Papyrus, 10, 11
Egyptian astronomy, 15
Egyptian chemistry, 28
Egyptian mathematics, 12–14
Egyptian medicine, 10–12
Egyptian technology, 14
Equations, cubic, 71, 74
Equations, indeterminate, 29, 30, 50–54
Equations, quadratic, 34, 47, 50, 66, 74
Equations, simple, 13, 34, 66
Equations, simultaneous, 34, 35
EUCLID, 65, 73, 80, 88, 89, 91
EULER, 53, 54
Evolution, 24
Eye, 30, 77, 81

FA-HSIEN, 29
Faience, 83
Falasifa, 61
Falconry, 87
Fāṭimid, 61, 70
FERMAT, 53, 54, 73
Fevers, 30, 31, 76, 77
Fihrist, 75
Five element theory, 23
FLAMSTEED, 91
Fractions, 8, 13, 29
FREDERICK II, 62, 78, 87
FRENICLE, 54
Fukudai, 94
GALEN, 11, 68, 76, 77, 89

GALILEO, 10, 40, 99
GANGOOLY, P., 38, 43
GEBER, 64, 65, 82, 89
Geography, 59, 67
Geology, 72
GERARD OF CREMONA, 72, 88
GERSON, LEVI BEN, 89
Ghazna, 62, 70
Ghubar numerals, 78
Giralda, 63
Gnomon, 10, 19, 39, 41, 42, 46, 58, 78
Granada, 62, 83
Grand Canal, China, 36
Gravity, Force of, 75
GREAVES, JOHN, 63, 79
Greeks, 5, 8, 10, 11, 15, 17–20, 22, 37, 38, 40, 42, 44, 52, 57, 63, 73, 98
Greenwich Observatory, 94
GROSSETESTE, ROBERT, 72
GUNDISALVO, 88
Gundishapur, 51, 60, 61, 68, 90
Gunpowder, 31, 32
Gupta, 44

ḤĀJJĪ PĀSHĀ, 82
HAMMURABI, 12
Han, 19, 20
HANKEL, H., 53
Harappā, 16
Harness, 20
Ḥarrān, 63, 67
HĀRŪN AL-RASHĪD, 64
HARVEY, WILLIAM, 82
HEARN, L., 99
Hearst Papyrus, 10
Heart, 82
Hebrew, 15, 22, 62, 76, 88, 89
Herbals, 31
HERODOTOS, 12
HERO(N), 65, 75
Hieratic, 12
Hieroglyphic, 12
Hindu astronomy, 30, 37–46
Hindu mathematics, 14, 15, 18, 30, 46–58, 71
Hindu medicine and surgery, 17, 58
Hindu technology, 58
HIPPARCHOS, 79, 93
Hippiatry, 83
HIPPOCRATES, 11, 12, 68
HIRE, P. DE LA, 91, 93
HOERNLE, RUDOLF, 54
HOMER, 98
Horticulture, 84
Hospitals, 82, 90
Hou Han Shu, 27
Hsia, 19
HSIA-HOU YANG, 29
HSÜAN-TSANG, 29
HUA SHOU, 31
HUA T'O, 30
HŪLĀGŪ, 78, 79, 85
HUME, 23
ḤUNAIN IBN ISḤĀQ, 65, 68
ḤUSAIN QULĪ KHĀN, 85
HU SSU-HUI, 31
HUYGHENS, 10
HYPATIA, 51

IBN AL-BAIṬĀR, 78
IBN AL-BANNĀ', 78, 84
IBN AL-HĀ'IM AL-FARAḌĪ, 84
IBN AL-HAITHAM (ALHAZEN), 70, 72, 73, 89
IBN AL-KHATĪB, 82
IBN AḶ-MAJDĪ, 84
IBN AL-MUNDHIR, 83
IBN AL-NAFĪS, 81, 82
IBN AL-QUNFŪDH, 84
IBN AL-SA'ĀTĪ, 76
IBN AL-SHĀṬIR, 84
IBN GABIROL, 69
IBN ḤAUQAL, 59
IBN HUDHAIL, 83

IBN JUZAYY, 83
IBN KHATIMAH, 82
IBN MAS'ŪD, JAMSHĪD, 85
IBN QURRA, 65, 80, 88
IBN RUSHD, 62, 76, 87
IBN SHAPRUT, 70
IBN SID, ISAAC, 87
IBN SĪNĀ, 62, 70–73, 77, 88
IBN TIBBON, JACOB BEN MAḤIR, 89
IBN TIBBON, MOSES, 89
IBN TIBBON, SAMUEL, 89
IBN WĀFID, 77
IBN YŪNUS, 70, 79
IBN YŪSUF, 81
IBN ZUHR (AVENZOAR), 76, 77
I-CHING, 29
I-HSING, 30
IKHWĀN AL-ṢAFĀ', 69
Indeterminate equations, 29, 30, 50–54
Inductive method, 1, 5
Indus Valley, 16, 71
Ink, 28, 34
Ionians, 22
Irrigation, China, 19, 36
Irrigation, 'Iraq, 85
'ISA THE MONGOL, 34
Istanbul, 86
I Wu Chih, 27
IZEKI CHISHIN, 97

JĀBIR IBN ḤAYYAN (GEBER), 64, 65, 82, 89
JAGANNĀTH, 91
Jaina, 22, 98
Jai Prakaś, 92, 93
Jaipur, 91
JAI SINGH, 91–94
Japanese mathematics, 35, 50, 94–97
Jewish translators, 86, 89
JOHN OF SEVILLE, 88
JOHNSON, M. C., 35
Jundīshāpūr (see Gundishapur)
JUSTINIAN, 28, 60
Jyā, 57, 90

Kahun Papyrus, 11
KAMĀL AL-DĪN, 78, 81
Karma, 25
KĀTYĀYANA, 17
KAUTILYA, 17
KAYE, G. R., 37, 43, 54, 56, 63
KEPLER, 72
KHALĪFA, 81
Khānbaliq, 36
Kitāb al-Manāẓir, 81
Kitāb al-shifā', 71
KO HUNG, 28
Korea, 33
KUBLAI KHĀN, 34–36
Kulliyat, 77
KUO SHOU-CHING, 34, 35
KURUSHIMA GITA, 97
Kuṭṭaka, 34, 46, 50, 52
KWANNO GENKEN, 95

LAGRANGE, 54
LALLA, 45
LĀṬADEVA, 39, 45
Lenses, 81
Leprosy, 31
LEUKIPPOS, 26
Libros del Saber de Astronomia, 87
LI CHIH (LI YEH), 34
Līlāwatī, 48, 49
LIU PIN, 32

Magnetic compass, 89, 90
MAHĀVĪRA, 47, 51
MAḤMŪD OF GHAZNA, 62, 70
MAIMONIDES, 77
MAÑJULA, 45
MANUEL, PADRE, 91
Manuscript, Bakhshālī, 54, 55
Maps, 31
Marāgha, 79

MARSHALL, SIR JOHN, 16
MĀSHALLĀH, 64
Materia medica, 11, 30, 77, 88
Mathematics, Babylonian, 8, 12, 15, 56
Mathematics, Chinese, 14, 29, 34, 35, 43, 94
Mathematics, Egyptian, 12–14
Mathematics, Hindu, 14, 15, 18, 30, 46–58, 71
Mathematics, Japanese, 35, 50, 94–97
Mathurā, 91
MATSUNAGA RYŌHITSU, 97
Mecca, 60
Mechanics, 75
Medicine, Arabic, 68, 70, 76, 77
Medicine, Babylonian, 12
Medicine, Chinese, 30, 31
Medicine, Egyptian, 10–12
Madinah, 60
MENELAOS, 89
MENON, C. P. S., 6, 21
Mercury, 10, 65
Merkhet, 15
Meru, 16, 21
Metallurgy, 14
Meteorology, 80, 89
MEYERHOF, M., 90
MEZIRIAC, B. DE, 53
MICHAEL SCOT, 87
MIKAMI, Y., 30, 97
Ming, 31
Mirrors, 20
Mohenjo-Daro, 16
Mohist, 20
Mongol astronomy, 35, 78, 79
Mongols, 32, 35, 36, 75, 78, 79
Monotheism, 22
Montpellier, 59
MOSES, JUDAH BEN, 87
MUḤYĪ AL-DĪN, 78
Mul-Apin, 9
Music, 23, 65, 71
Mutawassiṭāt, 80

NAGAOKA, 97
Nakshatras, 19
Naples, 62
Nara, 31
NĀṢIR AL-DĪN, 78–80
NAU, F., 56
NECKAM, ALEXANDER, 90
NEEDHAM, J., 26, 35
Negative quantity, 29, 34, 47, 54, 55
Nestorians, 34, 60, 68
NEUGEBAUER, O., 8
NEWTON, ISAAC, 40, 73
Nineveh, 7
Nippur, 7, 21
Notation, mathematical, 8, 13, 34, 54–57
Ñyāya, 25

Oculists, Syrian, 81
Ophthalmology, 81, 82
Optics, Arabic, 65, 72, 73
Optics, Chinese, 20
Oranges, 28
Order in Nature, 23, 25
Oxford, 63, 79

Padua, 72, 77, 89
Pahlawi (Pehlevi), 60, 64
Palermo, 78, 88
P'ANG AN-SHIH, 31
PĀNINI, 17
PAN KU, 24
Paper, 27
Papyri, mathematical, 11–14
Papyri, medical, 10, 11
PECKHAM, JOHN, 72
Pei-ping (Peking), 35
Pellian equation, 53
PHILO, 36, 75
Pictographic, 7, 16

PI SHENG, 32
Pităkăs, 25
Plague, 82
PLINY, 11
Portuguese, 88
Positional principle, 12, 56, 70
Printing, 32, 33
Problem Texts, 7
PTOLEMY, 40, 44, 57, 65, 67, 68, 73, 78–80, 86, 88, 91, 93
Pulse, 31, 77
Purāṇas, 17, 21
Pyramid, 10, 14, 21, 46
PYTHAGORAS, 8, 14, 18

QALONYMOS, 89
Qānūn, 71, 82, 89
Qibla, 84
Quadrant, 78, 79, 84
Quadratic equations, 34, 47, 50
Quadrilaterals, 46, 47
Qur'ān, 69, 88
QUṬB AL-DĪN, 78, 80, 81

Rainbow, 65, 80
RAMAN, SIR C. V., 97
RAMANUJAN, S., 97
RAYMOND. I., 62, 87
Refraction, 73, 80
REGIOMONTANUS, 67, 80
Regula falsi, 13
RENAUD, H. P. J., 84
RHAZES, 67, 68, 89
Rhind Papyrus, 11
RITTER, H., 83
River-Valley cultures, 5
ROBERT OF CHESTER, 88, 90
Roman, 21, 44
Rome (Rūm), 42, 60
RUSKA, JULIUS, 63

Sabaean, 63, 67
SACHAU, E., 38
ST. PAUL, 22
SALADIN, 77, 84
Saljuq, 74
Samarkand, 60, 62, 63, 79, 85, 91, 93
Samarrā, 67
SARTON, G., 13, 28, 57, 63, 68, 71, 80, 81
Sassānid, 43, 60, 85, 90
SAUSSURE, L. DE, 19
SAXL, F., 63
SEKI KŌWA, 94, 97
Seleucid, 9
SENGUPTA, P. C., 38, 39
SEVERUS SĒBŌKHT, 56
Seville, 62, 63, 76, 88
Sexagesimal, 7, 19
Sextant, 92
SHA-K'O-SHIH, 36
SHEN KUA, 32
Sicily, 62, 86
Siddhāntas, 37, 64
Siddhānta Śiromani, 48
Silk, 27
Simultaneous equations, 9
Sindhind, 37, 61
Sine, 57, 58, 90
Smallpox, 31, 68
SMITH, V., 43
SNELL, WILLEBRORD, 73, 74, 80
Sound, 69
Square cosmology, 5, 21
ŚRĪDHARA, 47, 48, 50
ŚRĪPATI, 45
STEIN, SIR AUREL, 27, 32
Suan-p'an, 29
Sui, 30, 57
Sultanganj, 58
Śulva-sūtras, 18
Sumerian, 6, 12, 16
Sun-dial, 41, 92
Sung, 32, 36
SUN TZU, 29
SUNG YÜN, 29
Sun Tzu Suan Ching, 51
Sūryaprajñapti, 21

Sūrya Siddhānta, 37–39, 41, 61
Suśruta, 17, 58
Sylvester, 94
Symbolism, algebraic, 85, 96
Syriac, 60, 78

Table Texts, 7, 9
Tables, Alphonsine, 87
Tables, Hakemite, 70
Tables, Ilkhānian, 79
Tables, Samarkand, 62, 85
Tables, Sinjaric, 76
Tables, Toledan, 70, 87
Taisei Sankyō, 95
Tamerlane (Tīmūr Lang), 85
T'ang, 30–32, 57
Taoism, 22–24, 27
Tao Tê Ching, 23
Ta'rīkh al-Hind, 71
Taxila (Takṣaśila), 17
Tea, 28
Technology, Chinese, 20
Technology, Egyptian, 14
tengen jutsu, 34
Thales, 22
Toita Yasusuke, 97
Toledo, 62, 70, 87–89
Trachoma, 82
Transmission of knowledge, 12, 29, 42, 61, 66, 69, 76, 85–90
Transmutation, 83
Trigonometry, 34, 79, 80, 88
Ts'ai Lun, 27
Ts'an T'ung Ch'i, 24
Tseng Kung-Liang, 31
Tun-Huang, 32
Tut'ankhamūn, 15
Tycho Brahe, 35

Ujjain (Ujjayinī), 40, 91
Ulūgh Beg, 62, 85, 91, 92
'Umar Khayyām, 66, 71, 74, 75
Umayyad, 61, 62, 69
Ur, 10
Uruk, 6
Utkramajyā, 41

Varāhamihira, 37, 39, 45
Vedāngas, 17, 37
Vedas, 6, 16, 17
Venice, 89
Veterinary science, 31, 83
Vieta, 80
Vīja-Ganita (see Bīja)

Wakhtang VI, 85
Wallis, 53, 54
Wang Hao-ku, 31
Wang Hsi, 36
Wang Hsiao-t'ung, 30
Wang Tao, 31
Water-clock, 10, 15, 75
Wei Po-Yang, 24
Whitney, 42
Windmills, 69
Witelo, 72
Wang Ch'in Jo, 32
Woolley, Sir Leonard, 10

Yang, 25
Yang Fu, 27
Yang Hui, 34
Yang Yi, 31
Yao, 19
Yantra, 92, 93
Yellow River, 19, 36
Yemen, 84
Yin, 25
Yüan, 35, 36
Yüan-Hsing, 27

Zero, 8, 50, 54, 56
Zīj Muhammad Shāhī, 92, 94
Zīj Ulūgh Beg, 85
Zodiac, 15
Zoroaster, 22